SCIENCE
THE SEARCH

Discovering the Principles
that Govern God's Creation

David Quine

BOOK 3 CAUSE & EFFECT

REVISED STUDENT DIRECTED TEXT

THE CORNERSTONE CURRICULUM PROJECT

BOOK 1 PROPERTIES
BOOK 2 INTERACTION & SYSTEMS
BOOK 3 CAUSE & EFFECT
BOOK 4 SCIENTIFIC THEORIES

Science: The Search — Book 3
Revised edition copyright © 1995 by David Quine
Published by The Cornerstone Curriculum Project
2006 Flat Creek Place, Richardson, Texas 75080
972-235-5149

To My Family — for your faithfulness to me as I wrote this series. A special thanks for always assembling the kits that accompany this program.

To My Parents — for allowing me as a child to always ask questions, some of which could be answered, while many that could not. Thanks for directing me towards science as I was growing up.

To Families who will use Science: The Search — for your desire to pass on to your children the spirit and tradition of Reformational scientists, to observe and to explore, knowing that to learn of His creation is to learn of His "invisible attributes".

To the late Dr. John W. Renner — science educator and author. A special thanks for allowing us to use several activities from his curriculum, Learning Science.

Contents

* Read the instructions for this activity before beginning Activity 1.

Preface

Children learn best by doing! SCIENCE: THE SEARCH **Book 3** is a student directed text in which your children learn about science by actually developing and testing their predictions to various problems. Lesson Plans are fully developed and are written directly to your children. Each activity includes **MATERIALS OR INFORMATION I NEED** and **WHAT I AM TO DO AND TO CONSIDER** so that your children can easily carry out each activity. The materials needed to complete each activity are mostly common household items.

Although there are many science curricula available, they can be classified into three groups.

TEXTBOOK APPROACH

1. Gives detailed, factual, information.
2. 'Speaks in' scientific nomenclature.
3. Children read about science
    — they memorize.

HANDS-ON APPROACH

COOKBOOK APPROACH

1. Many times the final conclusion of what is going to happen is given before the children begin the activity.
2. Children are given specific directions describing how to carry out the activity —they follow directions.

REASONING APPROACH

1. A problem is given for children to solve.
2. Leading questions give guidance and direction.
3. Children observe, describe, compare contrast, predict, classify, analyze, interpret, and formulate the main idea
    — they reason.

SCIENCE: THE SEARCH is a hands-on reasoning approach to science. Because the world was created by a reasonable God, children can find out something true about nature and the universe on the basis of reason. Children can find out about the world by observation and experimentation. This view of the created world was unique to Christianity, and became the soil for the birth of modern science.

SCIENCE: THE SEARCH using the reasoning approach actively involves your children the search for knowledge through the scientific processes without sacrificing the structure they need to guide their explorations and give meaning to their discoveries.

PHASE 1: EXPLORING THE CONCEPT —

Children are given materials and a problem to solve. They look for patterns and relationships. They observe, compare, contrast, predict, analyze, and begin formulating the main idea.

Parents are given a conversation to lead and guide the investigation. This provides direction to the exploration.

PHASE II: NAMING THE CONCEPT —

Parents are given the relationship between the exploration and the correct scientific terminology.

PHASE III: EXPANDING THE CONCEPT —

Children engage in additional investigations in order to correlate and apply this new knowledge. They continue to reason and analyze.

Parents are again given the conversation necessary to complete the investigation.

Suggested Teaching Schedule

♥ Do science one day per week.
♥ Set aside 1 to 2 hours for each class.
♥ The following schedule is only suggested.

Book 3 - 'Cause and Effect' is self directed. That means that the instructions are written directly to your child. As with previous books Cause and Effect focuses upon understanding and application. You will be called upon from time to time to assist your child with an activity. Every child is unique. Don't let the schedule dictate your child's pace. The schedule should only serve as a guide. Some sections will go faster while others slower.

I do recommend longer periods of instruction with only one day of instruction per week. This schedule allows time for your child to think about, to reflect on what has been taught. This 'thinking time' serves much like the time needed for bread to rise. Short periods of time only fragment the learning into meaningless parts. NOTE: The Life Science sections will require additional time during the week. In addition, some of the Life Science activities will go longer than one week. If it is possible to move to the next activity simply do so. Having two or more of these activities going on at the same time is okay.

Date	Week	Section	Activity	Date	Week	Section	Activity
_____	☐ 1	I	1	_____	☐ 19	III	18
_____	☐ 2		2	_____	☐ 20		19
_____	☐ 3		3	_____	☐ 21		20
_____	☐ 4		4	_____	☐ 22		21
_____	☐ 5	VARIABLES	5	_____	☐ 23	ENERGY	22
_____	☐ 6		6	_____	☐ 24		23
_____	☐ 7		7	_____	☐ 25		24
_____	☐ 8		8	_____	☐ 26		25
_____	☐ 9	II	9	_____	☐ 27		26
_____	☐ 10		10	_____	☐ 28		27
_____	☐ 11		11	_____	☐ 29	IV	28
_____	☐ 12		12	_____	☐ 30		29
_____	☐ 13	FACTORS	13	_____	☐ 31		30
_____	☐ 14		14	_____	☐ 32	FOOD	31
_____	☐ 15		15	_____	☐ 33		32
_____	☐ 16		16	_____	☐ 34		33
_____	☐ 17		17	_____	☐ 35		34
_____	☐ 18 — A catch up week —			_____	☐ 36 — A catch up week —		

9/9/94 Activity 1 - Powder

Properties
- *white*
- *shiny crystals*
- *some particles white but dull looking*
-

The mystery powder is composed of three different kinds of materials:

#1   *#2*   *#3*

SAMPLE

ACTIVITY 1
POWDER

MATERIALS
construction paper, dark
magnifier
mesh cloth, coarse and fine, cross stitch fabric (in kit)
mystery powder (parents are to mix-answer key)
rubber band
small jar, wide mouth preferred

OVERVIEW: EXPLORING THE CONCEPT - SUBSYSTEM

LESSON PLAN

MATERIALS OR INFORMATION I NEED	WHAT I AM TO DO AND TO CONSIDER
1. Have your parents make up the mystery powder. Have them turn to the answer key for the mixture.	
2. Do not tell them how many powders or the names of the powders at this time.	"Look at the powder in the jar. Use a magnifier to observe the powder."
	"What properties have you observed?"
	"List some of them in your observation notebook."
	"Do you think there is more than one type of powder? ... Why do you think so?"
	"Are all the particles the same kind?"
	"Look at these two pieces of cloth. What do you notice about the holes? How could you use the two pieces of cloth to separate particles of different sizes?"
	"If you were to use the screen to make a 'saltshaker', would you use the screen with the large or small holes first? ... Why do you think so?"
	"If you use the screen with the large holes first what do you think would happen? ... If you use the screen with the small holes first, what do you think would happen?"

"Using the screen with the small holes first will let the smallest particles come through but keep the largest particles inside the jar."

"Use the screens to separate the powders. As you 'shake' them out, put them into different piles."

"How many kinds of powder were in the jar? ... What evidence did you have?

"Objects can be put together to form systems. Call this your powder system."

"What are the properties of each of the powders?

"How is this powder (like or different from) this powder?"

"What do you think the powders are?
Why do you think so?"

"One powder is salt, one is baking powder, and one is oatmeal. Can you find each of the items?"

If you can not tell the name of each, then ask your parents for help.

"Put all the items back into the jar and save the mixture for Activity 2.

ACTIVITY 2
SUBSYSTEMS

MATERIALS
BTB, (Bromothymol Blue)
cross stitch fabric, coarse and fine
fruit basket with assorted fruits
magnifier
mixture from Activity 1
plastic spoon
small prescription vial
vinegar

OVERVIEW: NAMING THE CONCEPT - SUBSYSTEM

LESSON PLAN

MATERIALS OR INFORMATION I NEED	WHAT I AM TO DO AND TO CONSIDER
1. Have your parents make up a basket of fruit. The basket should have several types of fruit.	"This is a system." "What would be a good name for this system?" (Answer: Check the answer key.) "Pick up one piece of fruit from the basket. What kind of fruit is it? This '_____ ' is one part of the system." "Name other parts of the basket system."
2. The next time you and your family are sitting at the dinner table together....	"Your family makes up a system. What would be a good name for this system?" (Example: The Quine system) "You are one part of your system. How many parts are there in your family.? "If you were to name each part of your family, what would be good names for each?"
3. During the day ...	"Look for systems and parts to each system around your home. Record them in your observation notebook. At the end of the day see how many you have found."

4. Use the jar with the mixture
from Activity 1.

"This is the same powder that you observed in the last activity."

"What did you say was in it? Name the parts to this system."
(Answer: Check the answer key)

The idea:

"The parts of a system are called the

subsystems.

"What are the subsystems in your 'powder system'?"
(Answer: Check the answer key.)

"Name the subsystems in the fruit basket system."

"Name the subsystems in your family system."

"Name some of the subsystems that were in the systems you found around your home."

---

7. Squeeze a few drops of btb into a small cup of water ... Stir ...then add one drop of vinegar ... Stir. The water should be yellow. If not, add another drop of vinegar and stir.

"Pour some of the liquid into the jars containing the salt-baking powder-oatmeal mixture."

"What happened?"

"Was there any interaction?"

"What evidence do you have?"

"What do you think caused the liquid to change from yellow to light blue?"

---

8. The following conversation will help you set up and conduct an experiment to test your idea...

"Do you think the 'powder mixture system' interacted to make the color change, or only some of the parts?"

"What could you do to see if one or more of the subsystems caused the liquid to change from yellow to blue?"

9. If you did not suggest testing each subsystem separately then following the conversation below ,...

"Put some baking powder, oatmeal, and salt into separate jars."

"Make a sketch of your experiment. Be sure to write the subsystem name for each jar."

"Add some of the yellow liquid to each jar."

"Did the complete powder mixture interact to make the color change or was it one of the subsystems?"

"What evidence do you have to support your idea?"

"Write your observations under each jar."

10. You will need the mixture, a small plastic bag with tie (or zip lock), a vial, vinegar, and a tablespoon.

"Put one tablespoon of the powder system into the plastic bag."

"Fill the vial full of vinegar and set it into the plastic bag. Do not let it spill."

"Tie off the bag."

"What do you think will happen if the liquid interacts with the mixture?"

"Pour the liquid on the mixture and observe any changes within the system."

"What happened?"

This experiment if similar to the one outlined in steps 8 and 9.

"What do you think caused the bubbles and the bag to inflate?"

"Design an experiment to find out if the complete powder system caused the interaction or if one of the subsystems caused the change."

ACTIVITY 3
CLOUDY-NOT CLOUDY

MATERIALS
baking soda
chalk, crushed
clay
construction paper, dark
blue, red, or green food coloring
filter paper
jars with lids, 8
magnifier
powdered milk
salt
spoon
starch, powdered
sugar

OVERVIEW: EXPANDING THE CONCEPT - SUBSYSTEM

LESSON PLAN

MATERIALS OR INFORMATION I NEED	WHAT I AM TO DO AND TO CONSIDER
1. Set the following items on a piece of dark construction paper: baking soda chalk, crushed clay powdered milk salt Starch, powdered sugar	
	"Observe the materials with the magnifier."
	"Pour water into each of the jars."
	"Put a small amount of each material into separate jars."
	"Make a sketch of the eight jars and label the contents of each."
	"Stir and describe what happens to each."
	"Can you see through each of them?"

"Which mixtures are clear ...cloudy? ... Colored or colorless? ... Can the mixture be both clear and colored?"

"Record your observations under each drawing."

"Put lids on each jar. Set them to the side for several days and see what happens to them."

2. After a couple of days ...

"Look carefully at each jar and compare them to the drawings from your observational notebook."

"What has happened? ... Have any changed? ... Describe the changes?"

"Record in your notebook any changes that you see."

3. Focus you attention on one of the vials that is clear on the top and cloudy or solid on the bottom ...

"Look specifically at this system."

"How many different parts do you see?"

"Each part is a subsystem of the system."

"What do you think will happen if you shake the jar? Why do you think so?"

4. Gently shake the jar...

"See what happens?"

"If you let it set for a couple of days, what do you think will happen?"

5. Find a jar that is clear ...

"What is in this jar?"

"Will shaking this jar have any affect on it? Why? ... Try it."

The idea

"If when water and another material are stirred together they make a clear mixture, the mixture is called a

Solution.

A solution is a special kind of mixture.

"Which of the jars contain solutions? Why are these solutions?

6. Pick up a cloudy jar …

'What do you think? … Is this a solution? Why not?"

"A cloudy mixture is called a

Nonsolution."

"Are there any other nonsolutions?"

---

7. Some optional activities …

"Pour some soft drink (a non-cola is best) into a glass. What do you observe? … Do you think this is a solution or a nonsolution?"

"Put a tea bag into a clear glass of hot water. Observe what happens … Take the tea bag out of the water. Describe the water - tea mixture. Is it a solution or nonsolution? Why do you think so? Name the subsystems."

"Be on the lookout for examples of solutions and nonsolutions."

---

8. You will need the following items:
Jar, 2
Salt, 1/2 teaspoon
Chalk dust, 1/2 teaspoon
Water
Paper towel, cut into a circle
Funnel, if you have one
Magnifier
Pie tin

"Observe the salt and chalk dust with the magnifier."

"Make a chalk-salt-water system."

"Shake the jar. Describe the mixture."

"Is it a solution or nonsolution?"

"Why do you think so?"

"Name each subsystem."

"How could you separate the subsystems?"

"You will use the paper towel to make a filter paper."

"Fold it in half."

"Fold it in half again."

"Open it up so that it is in the shape of a funnel."

"Set the funnel-shaped filter paper in your funnel."

Do NOT taste any mixture unless you know
the contents are safe.

"Set the funnel over the empty jar. "

"What do you think will happen if you pour the
nonsolution into the funnel?"

"Now pour the chalk-salt-water mixture into the
funnel and observe what happens."

"What do you observe on the filter paper?"

"Where is the salt?"

"Look at the liquid that passed through the filter
paper. ... Describe how it looks. ... Is it a solution or a
nonsolution?"

"Put your finger into the liquid and then touch your
finger to your tongue."

"Describe how it tastes."

"What does your observation lead you to believe
about the salt."

"How could you get the salt from the salt-water
mixture?"

"Pour some of the salt-water mixture into a pie tin
... Now set it in the sun until it evaporites."

After the water evaporates ...

"Using the magnifier describe what is in the lid."

"What do you think is in the lid?"

Compare these crystals with some salt crystals.
What do you think is in the lid? What evidence do
you have that this is salt?"
(Answer: Salt. The shape of the crystals.)

ACTIVITY 4
A SPECIAL SOLUTION

MATERIALS
jar
measuring cup
measuring spoons
pan
salt
sponge
sugar
thermometer
water

OVERVIEW: EXPANDING THE CONCEPT - SUBSYSTEM

LESSON PLAN

MATERIALS OR INFORMATION I NEED	WHAT I AM TO DO AND TO CONSIDER
1. You will need the materials listed above.	"How much sugar will water dissolve?"
	"How could you find out?"
	"Measure about 1/8 cup of water."
	"Using the 1/8 teaspoon add sugar and stir until no more sugar will dissolve."
	"How much sugar is in the solution?"
	"Add a little more sugar."
Save the solution!	"Observe the sugar."
	"Describe what happens."
2. This is a variation of the first experiment.	"How much salt do you think water will dissolve?"
	"Do you think the water will dissolve more salt than sugar? ... Why do you think so?"
	"Repeat the first experiment using salt." "What did you find out?"
Save the solution!	"Is it what you expected?"

3. Give your children the sponge, a measuring cup, and a pan.

"How much water can this sponge hold?"

"How could you find out?"

"Try it and see what happens."

"Can it hold any more?"

"The sponge is completely soaked."

"When the sponge soaks up all it can hold, it is said to be

Saturated."

"Water (or any liquid) can dissolve just a certain amount of a substance such as salt or sugar. When it has dissolved all it can hold, the mixture is called a

Saturated solution."

Use the sugar-water system.

"I wonder if it is possible to dissolve any more sugar in your system?"

Caution: Parents!
Introduce the thermometer.
When working with heat,
parents should provide as much help as necessary to prevent anyone from being injured.

"What is the temperature of the water?"

"What do you think would happen if the water was hotter?"

"Pour the sugar-water system into the pan and carefully begin to heat it on the stove."

"Heat the system to 50 degrees Celsius."

"See if the heated water will dissolve more sugar."

"Heat the system to 90 degrees Celsius.:

"Do you think it will hold more sugar now?"

"Try it and see?"

"How much sugar will dissolve in water?"

"What difference does temperature make on the amount of sugar dissolved?"
(Answer: Check the answer key.)

"Now the solution is called a

Super saturated solution.

"What do you think would happen if your super saturated solution was to became very cold?"

"Pour the hot super saturated sugar-water system into a glass."

"Set the glass into a large sauce pan."

"Put ice cubes around the glass in the sauce pan and then pour some water into the pan."

"Put the thermometer in the glass."

"Carefully observe the saturated solution as the temperature goes down."

What do you see happening?"

---

4. If you have some fresh fruit then add some lemon and lime juice to the sugar-water system pour it over the fruit and enjoy a snack. As you do, tell your parents about a solution, a non-solution, and a supersaturated solution.

"What is a solution?"

"What effect does temperature have on a solution."

---

5. Go back to the salt-water system.

"What do you think would happen to your salt-water system if it were heated? Would more salt dissolve? Why do you think so?"

"Try it and see."

ACTIVITY 5
SWINGING SYSTEMS

MATERIALS
a large swing
a stop watch, or a watch with a second hand

OVERVIEW: EXPLORING & NAMING THE CONCEPT - VARIABLES

LESSON PLAN

MATERIALS OR INFORMATION I NEED	WHAT I AM TO DO AND TO CONSIDER
1. Go with your family to a park that has large swings. You might consider asking your mom to pack a large picnic basket. Swing for a few moments.	"Describe the swing." "Objects can be put together to form a group of related objects. Such a group of objects is called a system. For example, the seat, chain, and bars of this swing make up a system. The objects in this system interact when you set in the seat and you swing. Call this your swinging system. As you swing there is interaction" "The parts of a system are called the subsystems. Name the subsystems of your interacting swinging system." (Answer: Check the answer key.) "How does the swing system work?"
2. Set on the seat ... Go back and stop when you come back to the starting point. Note: During the remainder of this activity, make sure you do not push ('pump') as you swing.	"One complete swing, one back and forth movement, is called a **Cycle**." "Swing for a few seconds ... Count the number of cycles you go." "See how long it takes to go one cycle."

Using your stop watch, time one cycle.

"How long did it take?"

"A more accurate way to measure a cycle is to find the time it takes to go 10 cycles and then divide by 10."

"Try it again."

"How long did it take?"

"The **time** needed to make one cycle is the

Period."

"What is the period of your swinging system?"

"Do you think there might be a way to change the swinging system so that it will have a different period?"

"Try one or two of your ideas."

Remember!
Do NOT pump as you swing!

"How did you change the swinging system? What affect did it seem to have on the period?"

The idea

"As you have observed, the parts of a system can differ. For example, you can start out swinging from different heights, or the amount of weight in the swing can be different."

"A part of a system that can be arranged in different ways is called a

Variable."

You will need the help of another person.

"Look more closely at some of the variables of the swinging system."

"Sit in the seat."

With you in the seated, be pulled back higher than before..

Using a stop watch or a watch with a second hand...

"What is a cycle?"
(Answer: One back and forth movement.)

"Count the number of cycles you go in one minute."

"You count the number of cycles ... I will time your swing."

"How many complete back and forth movements did you go in one minute?"

This time be raised even a little higher.

"What difference do you think it would make if you are let you go from here? ... Do you think you would swing more times, less times, or the same number of times in one minute?"

"Why do you think so?"

"See what happens. You count the cycles while I time you."

"It should have been the same or about the same each time.."

"Is that what you expected?"

"I wonder why it was about the same each time?"

Be pulled back even higher.

"I wonder ... will it make a difference this time? What do you think?"

"Let's test your idea to see if it makes any difference."

"How many complete cycles did you go this time?"

"In this experiment what was the variable....what did you change?"
(Answer: Check the answer key.)

"What do you think? ... Does where I release you seem to make any difference in the number of swings in one minute?"

"Make a statement about the distance you are pulled back and the number of cycles you go in one minute."
(Answer: Check the answer key.)

3. Pull your child back....release your child.

"How many cycles do you think you will go in one minute? ... Why do you think so?"

"You count the number of cycles."

"Did you predict correctly?"

4. Now have two children (or a heavier person) sit in one swing seat. Pull them back any distance.

"What part of the system have you changed? What variable are you investigating?"
(Answer: Check the answer key.)

"Since there is more weight in the swing, weight is the variable you will investigate."

"Do you think you will swing more times, fewer times, or the same number of times in one minute?"

"Why do you think so?"

"I will time you while you count the cycles."

"How many complete cycles did you go?"

"Is it what you expected?"

"I wonder…why did you go about the same number of cycles?"

"Change the weight again to see if you get the same results."

"Is it what you had expected?"

"So far you have found that neither the point at which the seat is raised nor the weight in the seat seems to have any effect on the number of swings in one minute."

---

5. Throw the swing over the top bar one time so that the swing will be shorter. Observe the swing system now..

"How is the swing system different now?"

"Do you think that you would swing more times, fewer times, or the same number of times in one minute with the shorter swing?"

"Why do you think so?"

---

6. Sit in the seat and test your prediction.

"You count the cycles and I will time you for one minute."

"How many complete cycles did you swing? Is it more times, fewer times, or the same number of times as before?"

"Is that what you expected?"

---

7. Throw the swing over the top bar another time.

"Is the swing longer or shorter?"

"Will you swing more times, fewer times, or the same number of times with the swing like this?"

"Why do you think so?"

"Test your idea."

"What did you find out?"

"What were the three variables that you tested?"
(Answer: Check the answer key.)

"Describe how changing each variable changes the number of cycles in one minute?"
(Answer: Check the answer key.)

"What caused the cycle of the swinging system to change?"

"Can you explain why increasing the weight seems to have little or no effect on the number of swings in one minute?"

"What about the release point? Why would the number of swings in one minute be the same or about the same?"

"What was the effect of changing the length of the swing?"

ACTIVITY 6
BOUNCING SYSTEMS

MATERIALS
basketball
golf ball
soccer ball
tennis ball
yard stick or meter stick

OVERVIEW: EXPANDING THE CONCEPT - VARIABLES

LESSON PLAN

MATERIALS OR INFORMATION I NEED	WHAT I AM TO DO AND TO CONSIDER

1. You will need all the materials listed above. You may need to ask someone to help you make the measurements..

"Which ball do you think will bounce the highest?"

"Drop the four balls on a hard floor several times."

"What do you observe?"

"Do you think that dropping the balls from different heights is a variable that will effect the bounce of a ball?"

You are to drop the ball from each level 5 times and find the average. The average is found by adding each distance and dividing by 5.

Basketball

1 2 3 4 5 average

Knee level:

Waist level:

Nose level:

Make a similar chart for each type of ball.

"Drop the balls from knee level, from waist level, and then from nose level....use the yard stick to measure how high the ball bounces."

"How does the bounce of the ball vary with how high you hold the ball?"

"Give evidence that distance above the floor is a variable.

"Which ball bounces the highest? Which ball bounces the lowest?"

"Arrange the balls in order from the one that bounced the most to the least."

"What were the variables you investigated?" (Answer: Check the answer key.)

"Which ball bounced the highest?...the lowest?"

"Let's compare these two balls again."

"You take the best ball and drop it from knee level."

"How high did it bounce?"

"Now take the ball that bounced the least and drop it from your nose level."

"How high did this ball bounce?"

"Was it better than the first ball?"

"Now which ball bounced the highest?"

"Was this a fair comparison?"

"To compare the bounce of the two balls is it necessary to keep the dropping height the same?"

"From this last experiment can you tell which ball will bounce the highest? ... Why not?"

"Okay, this time you will drop them from the same level."

"For this experiment use the ball which bounced the highest and the one which bounced the lowest."

"Drop both of them from your waist level?"

"Drop mine one the bounced the lowest first. .

"How high did it bounce?"

"Now I want you to drop the other ball on the carpet or rug."

"Drop this ball."

"How high did your ball bounce?"

The idea:

"Which ball would you say has the greatest bounce? What do you think?"

"Was the last comparison a fair comparison?"

"What property of these balls were you investigating?"

"What variables did you investigate?"
(Answer: Check the answer key)

"To make a fair comparison of the how much a ball bounces what must you do?"
(Answer: Check the answer key.)

"When one variable is kept the same for several investigations, it is called a

Controlled variable."

"If you were going to run a race to see who was fastest. Would it be fair for one person to start 30 seconds before you begin? ... Why not? ... What about if you had to run around one block and the other person had to run around two blocks?"

"What are some of the variables you would need to control in a race?"
(Answer: Check the answer key)

"Why is it important to control all but one variable in an experiment?"

"If more than one variable is allowed to change in an experiment, is it possible to determine the appropriate cause?"

ACTIVITY 7
MORE BOUNCING

MATERIALS
silly putty
food coloring
yard or meter stick

OVERVIEW: EXPANDING THE CONCEPT - VARIABLES

LESSON PLAN

MATERIALS OR INFORMATION I NEED	WHAT I AM TO DO AND TO CONSIDER
1. You will need the materials listed above.	"What affect does the size of the ball have on how high it will bounce?"
	"Do you think a large ball will bounce higher than a small ball?"
	"Why do you think so?"
	"If you were to test your idea, would it be important for all the balls to be made from the same material?"
	"Make four 'silly putty' balls of different sizes and colors."

2. Keep track of your observations:

Ball	Distance of Fall	Height of Bounce
1 (largest)	1 yard or meter	
2	1 yard or meter	
3	1 yard or meter	
4 (smallest)	1 yard or meter	

"Name the variables you are investigating?"
(Answer: Check the answer key.)

"Which variables must you control?"
(Answer: Check the answer key.)

"Let's drop each ball from a height of one yard."

"Observe and measure the height of each bounce ... Keep track of your observations in your notebook."

"What did you find out?"

"Arrange the balls in order from the most bouncey to the least bouncey."

"Did you control for color?"
(Answer: No.)

"Do you think it was necessary to control for color? Why or why not?"

ACTIVITY 8
ANOTHER SWINGING SYSTEM

MATERIALS
string
scissors
stop watch, or watch with a second hand
washers

OVERVIEW: EXPANDING THE CONCEPT - VARIABLES

LESSON PLAN

MATERIALS OR INFORMATION I NEED	WHAT I AM TO DO AND TO CONSIDER

You will need the materials listed above.
If you need help conducting the experiments,
just ask your parents.

1.

"What are some of the properties of this washer?"

"What are some of the properties of the string?"

"Put the string and washer together to form a system by tying one washer to the end of the string."

"Describe your system? ... What are the subsystems?"

"There is interaction between the washer and the string."

"Do the objects interact by themselves?"

"This new system is called a

Pendulum."

"What variables do you think affect the swing of the pendulum?"

"What affect do you think each variable will have on the system?"

"Experiment with the system to determine the properties of the pendulum system."

"What variables did you investigate?"
(Answer: Check the answer key.)

"When you investigate the weight of the pendulum, which variables should you keep the same?"
(Answer: The length of the string and the release point.)

"When you investigate the release point, which variables should you control?"

"When you investigate the length of the string, which variables should you control?"

Design and conduct an experiment to determine what affects the swing of a pendulum.

The Pendulum System

POSSIBLE VARIABLE	PREDICTION	OBSERVATION	EXPLANATION
Weight			
Release Point			
Length of String			

"Which variable or variables affect the swing of the pendulum system?
(Answer: Check the answer key.)

"What would have happened if the length of the string were not controlled?"

Which variables did not seem to affect the swing of the pendulum?"
(Answer: Check the answer key.)

"Does this system remind you of another system you investigated?
(Answer: Check the answer key)

The idea:

"Some variables seem to make no difference in the outcome of an experiment while other do. The variables which do make a difference and which must be controlled are called

Relevant variables."

"When a relevant variable is overlooked in an experiment, the results of an experiment can be wrong."

"Why is it important to control some variables in an experiment?"

"Begin looking for variables that affect your life."

*ACTIVITY 9
PLANTS AND ANIMALS
AROUND YOUR HOME

MATERIALS
thermometer

OVERVIEW: EXPLORING & NAMING THE CONCEPT - ENVIRONMENTAL FACTORS

EXPANDING THE CONCEPT: VARIABLES

LESSON PLAN

MATERIALS OR INFORMATION I NEED	WHAT I AM TO DO AND TO CONSIDER

1. So that your children will begin to gain the big picture of the interaction between the climate and environment upon plants and animals, this activity should be conducted for three continuous months of the year on a regular basis. Of course the greatest changes occur in the transition from fall to winter or winter to spring. Select the three best months for your area of the country.

Choose a small, convenient place - your backyard, a field, a vacant lot, or an undeveloped section of a park.

The observations will be of two types:

Type 1: General observations ...
These observations should be made once or twice a month at the same location.

"During the year you will be observing the many plants and animals that live in your area. When plants and animals are grouped together they are called
Organisms."

"Record the conditions under which you find the different plants and animals."

2. Have your children answer these questions each time they visit this area. This will help them to look for changes as well as review the concepts developed in science the search: Properties and interaction and systems..

"What kinds of animals did you find? Describe the animals and the place where you found them." (Answer: I found many 'rolly-pollees' beneath a rock. The ground was moist. Since they were under the rock, it was dark.)

"What kinds of plants did you find?…describe them."

"What else was nearby?"

"What was the area like? ... Wet? ... Dry? ... Sunny? ... Warm? ... Cool?"

"What changes have taken place since your last observations? ... Do you notice anything else?"

Type two: Quantity observations …
In addition to the general observations, it will be important for your children to begin collecting information about precipitation, and air and ground temperatures. Monthly averages will be best for making general observations about these changes.

It would be best to have your children collect the data on their own (between 11:00 am and 2:00 pm is best); however, you may have your children use the weather report from the newspaper or television to record the daily precipitation and temperatures for your city. If you use a report, have your children find the average daily air temperature, by adding the high and low temperature and dividing by two.

If the precipitation is snow, bring in inside to melt before you measure the amount.

"Each day you will measure and record the amount of precipitation, the air temperature and the ground temperature."

"It is important to make these observations at about the same time each day."

"To measure the air temperature, set the thermometer about three feet above the ground. You will know it has reached the surrounding temperature when the thermometer stops going up or down. It may take several minutes to happen."

"To find the ground temperature remove about 2 inches of soil. Set the thermometer in the hole and place the removed soil on top of the thermometer end. Wait until the thermometer reading becomes constant before you take the reading."

"To find the amount of precipitation, set out a pan with vertical sides. Use a ruler to measure the amount each day. After you take your reading, pour the water out of the pan."

"Make a chart to keep a record of the data.

Date   temperature   precipitation
        Air   ground

QUANTITY DATA			

4. After completing the three months of observations...

"Let's look at your notes on the organisms around your home."

"You have collected two kinds of data."

"One type is a general description. This description tells about the qualities, or properties and is called

Qualitative data.

"The other type of data tells the amount or quantity. It consists of measurements. This type of data is called

Quantitative data.

"During the three months what qualitative changes did you observe?"
(Answer: For example, the grass changed from green to brown; the tree lost its leaves; the flowers stop blooming, etc.)

"It is often easier to understand data if it is placed onto a graph. The air temperature and ground temperature should be line graphs. Put the data on the same graph paper. To distinguish between them either use different color markers or use a solid line for one set of data and dashed for the other. The amount of precipitation should also be on the same graph but it should be a bar graph."

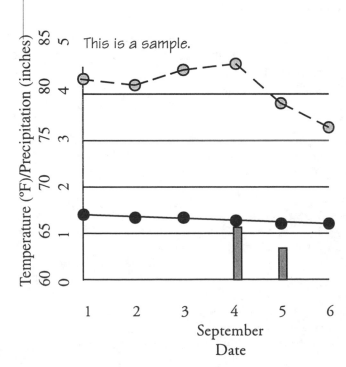

This is a sample.

Temperature (°F)/Precipitation (inches)

September
Date

"Look at the graphs. Do you see any major changes in the quantitative data? ... How would you describe these changes?"
(Answer: Check the answer key)

"Did you notice any changes in either the animals or the plants?"

"What do you think could have caused these changes in the plants and animals?"

"Could the changes in air or ground temperatures have some affect?"

"How about the amount of moisture?"

The idea -

"Do you think temperature and moisture could be variables that affect organisms?"

"Variables that affect the environment are called

Environmental factors."

---

6. Ask your parents to show you two or more of the same type plants or trees that were planted at about the same time but are different sizes...

"How are they different? ... They were planted at the same time and were about the same size."

"What do you think could have caused these two plants to grow differently?"
(Answer: Check the answer key.)

"How could you design some experiments to test the affect of these environmental factors on the growth of plants?"

ACTIVITY 10
PLANT GROWTH & MOISTURE

MATERIALS
medicine dropper
planter cups, 10 (or Styrofoam cups)
potting soil
ruler
tomato seeds, 20

OVERVIEW: EXPANDING THE CONCEPT - ENVIRONMENTAL FACTORS

LESSON PLAN

MATERIALS OR INFORMATION I NEED	WHAT I AM TO DO AND TO CONSIDER
	"Do you think that the amount of water a plant receives affects its growth?"
	"Can a plant have too much water? ... What about not enough water?"
	"Do you think that there might be a 'best' amount of water for a plant?"
The ability to design experiments seems to depend upon a persons age, experiences, and reasoning ability. You may need the assistance of your parents in designing experiments. The following conversation should help you in this investigation.	
	"How could you design an experiment to determine the effect of different amounts of water on the growth of plants?"
	"Are there variables or factors that might affect the growth of plants that you should control?" (Answer: Check the answer key.)
	"Do you think that the amount of light a plant receives could affect its growth?"
	"To make sure it does not interfere with your current test of moisture, you need to control for the amount of light your plants receive. You need to make sure that each plant receives the **same amount of light**."
	"What about the amount of fertilizer? ... If you give fertilizer, should you give each plant the same amount? ... Why do you think so?"

1. Obtain the materials listed on the previous page..

"Do you think the amount of heat might affect the growth? ... What could you do to control for heat?"

"You will need some tomato seeds, potting soil, and 10 planters."

"Put the same amount of soil into each planter cup."

"Plant two seeds in each cup."

"Line up the cups on a small cookie sheet."

"What variable or factor are you investigating?" (Answer: Check the answer key.)

"What variables are you going to control?" (Answer: Check the answer key.)

"Be sure that everything is the same except for the amount of moisture."

"Give the first two cups no water. Using a marker, write 'O' on the outside of these cups."

"Give the next two cups 1/8 teaspoon each. Write '1/8' on the outside of each of these cups."

"Put 1/4 teaspoon of water in the next two cups. Write '1/4' on the outside of each of these cups."

"Put 3/8 teaspoon of water in the next two cups. Write '3/8' on these cups."

"Put 1/2 teaspoon of water in the last two cups and write '1/2' on the outside of each."

"Put them in lighted area - but not in direct sunlight."

"Do you think that some will grow better than others? ... Which do you think will grow the best? ... Why do you think so?"

"You will not add any more water to the plants until your experiment is completed."

"Water the seeds with the appropriate amounts of water every other day. As you water be sure to look for evidence of growth."

After about one week...

"It is about time to evaluate your experiment."

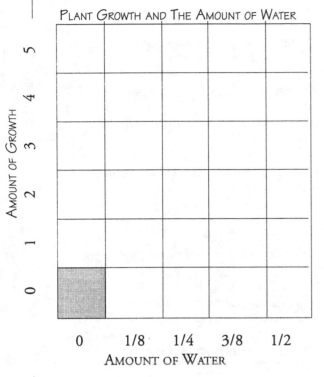

PLANT GROWTH AND THE AMOUNT OF WATER

AMOUNT OF GROWTH

AMOUNT OF WATER

Continue with the remaining plants until the chart if complete.

"Which tomato plants grew the most? ... The least? Did any not grow at all?
Does there seem to be a best amount of water?"

"What do you conclude about water and the growth of tomato plants?"

"You need to represent your observations so that others can quickly and easily see what happened in your investigation."

"The amount of water is recorded on the bottom of the chart."

"The amount of growth is up the side. '1' represents the least amount of growth ... '5' represents the most amount of growth."

"Look at the four plants that received no water.

"Did they grow the least, the most. Or somewhere in between?"

"Shade the box on the chart that would represent how well the plants that received 'no water' grew."

"What about the next group of plants - those receiving 1/8 teaspoons of water? ... Did they grow the least, the most, or somewhere in between? Which square should you shade to represent these plants?

"What was the least amount of water that you used? ... The most amount of water ?"

"The lowest amount to the highest amount is called the

Range.

"In your investigation the amount of moisture ranged from 0 to 1/2 teaspoon."

"Which amounts of water seem to be 'best' for the tomato seeds?"

"The range of water that seems to cause the 'best' growth is called the

Optimum range.

You will need a ruler.

"This chart represents **qualitative data** about the affect of water on the growth tomato seeds."

"How could you use your ruler to record

Quantitative data."

"Measure in millimeters the height of the four plants that received no water."

"What was the average height of these plants."

"Add the heights of the four plants and divide by four."

Graph paper…

"Use the graph paper to record this amount on the line above 'O' water."

Measure the height to find the average for each group of plants.

"Do the same thing for each of the other groups of plants."

"What was the **range** for this investigation? … What was the **optimum range**?

"Which chart shows **qualitative data** … **quantitative data?**"

"The amount of moisture was the environmental factor being investigated in this experiment.

"What can you conclude about the initial growth of tomato seeds and the amount of water?"

If it is the proper time of the year, you may want to plant your tomato plants outdoors and enjoy some fresh tomatoes later in the season. Or continue to have them grow in your home until a proper time to transplant.

"All the pots contained the same kind of seeds - tomato seeds."

"If, instead of using tomato seeds, you used seeds from a flowering plant from your locality, such as zinnia seeds, do you think you would get the same results?"

"Why do you think so?"

"How would you find out?"

You may wish to use seeds from some lovely flowering plant that can be transferred to a window box at a later time.

"Repeat this activity using seeds from several different kinds of plants."

ACTIVITY 11
AMOUNT OF SEEDS

MATERIALS
cups, 3 of the same size
potting soil
seeds, sunflower seeds are fun to use

OVERVIEW: EXPANDING THE CONCEPT - ENVIRONMENTAL FACTORS

LESSON PLAN

MATERIALS OR INFORMATION I NEED	WHAT I AM TO DO AND TO CONSIDER
1. Obtain the materials listed above.	"Prepare the cups with potting soil."
	"Plant only two seeds in one of the cups. Write '2' on the outside."
	"Plant six seeds in one of the other cups. Write '6' on the outside of this cup."
	"Plant twenty four seeds in the last cup. Write '24' on the outside of this cup."
	"Care for the plants in exactly the same way. Give each cup the same amount of water, light, fertilizer, etc."
	"What factor are you investigating in this experiment?" (Answer: Check the answer key.)
	"What is the range of seeds."
	"In which cup do you think the plants will grow best?"
	"Observe the growth of the plants for the next couple of weeks."
Look at the cup with two seeds.	"How many seeds were planted in this cup?"
	"How many plants grew?"
	"Did all the seeds grow into plants?"

Look at the cup with six seeds...

"How many seeds did you plant in this cup?"

"How many plants grew in this cup?"

"Did all the seeds grow into plants in this cup?"

Look at the cup with twenty-six seeds...

"How many seeds did you plant in this cup?"

"How many plants grew?"

"Did all the seeds grow into plants in this last cup?"

"Describe the number of plants from seeds using these terms - 'all', 'most, 'some', or 'none'. For example, in the cup with two seeds, all the seeds became plants."

Complete the chart to represent your observations.

Number of plants that grew			
Number of plants planted	2	6	26
Percentage of plants grew			

Calculate the percentage of growth by dividing the number of plants in the cup by the number of seeds planted in that cup. Then multiply that answer by 100.

Note: Percents are not easy to calculate nor easy to understand. If you need additional explanation, ask your parents.

"Use the chart to describe how many seeds became plants."

"For each group would you describe their growth as tall? ... Medium? ... Or short?"

"Is this type of description **qualitative** or **quantitative**?"

"How could you record your findings as quantitative data?"

Use the ruler....

"Use the ruler to find the plant height for each cup."

"To find the average height per cup add all the heights of the plants in a cup and then divide by the number of plants in the cup."

"Record your observations on a chart and on a graph."

"Make a general statement about the number of seeds and plant growth? ... Give both qualitative and quantitative data to support what you write."

ACTIVITY 12
PLANTS & FOODS

MATERIALS
containers, quart , 4
flowering plants, 4 of the same kind -choose your favorite, African violets & geraniums are some of
our favorites - they need to be as nearly alike as possible
plant food, either naturally occurring or man made
NOTE: rain water is needed for Activity 14.

OVERVIEW: EXPANDING THE CONCEPT - ENVIRONMENTAL FACTORS

LESSON PLAN

MATERIALS OR INFORMATION I NEED	WHAT I AM TO DO AND TO CONSIDER
1. Go with your parents to your local nursery to select four of your favorite plants. They need to be as nearly alike as possible. Also purchase some plant food. Ask the nurseryman for details.	"These plants are called ....Describe them." "You know that people and animals need vitamin and minerals. What about plants?"
2. When you get home....	"This plant food calls for [1 tablespoonful per quart of water]." "You will make up three different mixtures. "Pour one tablespoon of the plant food into one quart container of water. Label it '1 t per quart.'" "Pour two tablespoons of the plant food into another quart container of water. Label it '2 t per quart.'" "In the third quart container of water pour 1/2 tablespoon of the plant food and label it '1/2 t per quart.'" "In the fourth quart container of water you will put no plant food. Label it 'no plant food.'" "Each plant will receive a different amount of the plant food. When you water you will use the water from these jars."

"Be sure that everything else is the same. You are testing only one variable."

"What is the one variable you are investigating? (Answer: Amount of plant food.)"

3. Make available the four plants. Help your children label the pots:

#1 - no plant food
#2 - 1/2 t per quart
#3 - 1 t per quart
#4 - 2 t per quart

"Label the plants according to the amount of tablespoons of the plant food per quart container."

"Water the plants using the appropriate water - plant food container. Be sure to keep the soil moist but not overly wet."

"Observe their growth for the next month and record any changes that you see."

"Except for the amount of plant food, have all the conditions been the same?"

"Are you beginning to see any changes?"

"Does the amount of the plant food a plant receives make a difference in its growth, development, or color."

"Can a plant receive [too little - too much] plant food? ... What evidence do you have to support your idea?"

"What was the range of the plant food you tested?" (Answer: 0 to 2 tablespoonfuls per quart of water)

"Can you see an optimum range?" (Answers will vary.)

"In nature where do plants get their foods?"

ACTIVITY 13
PLANTS & FOODS CONTINUED
(This activity must follow the completion of ACTIVITY 13)

MATERIALS
bucket, large enough to collect a gallon of rain water
tin can, 3
potting soil
hammer and one very small nail
coleus cutting (begonia cutting will also work), 2
jars, 2

OVERVIEW: EXPANDING THE CONCEPT - ENVIRONMENTAL FACTORS

LESSON PLAN

MATERIALS OR INFORMATION I NEED	WHAT I AM TO DO AND TO CONSIDER
	"One way that plants are different from people and animals is that they can not move around to find food."
	"You saw that plant foods are important for the growth and development of plants."
	"Where do plants and trees outside get their food?"
	"Many people think that foods for plants come from either rainwater or the ground. How could you test to find the source of foods for plants?"
1. If you have not collected rain water, you need to do so now.	
2. Obtain the necessary materials.	"Punch very small holes in the bottom of a tin can."
	"Put nylon hose in the bottom of the can."
	"Fill the can with potting soil."
	"Set the can with the potting soil over another can."
	"Slowly pour about one quart of rainwater into the can with the potting soil. Let the water drain through the soil into the second container."
	"Pour this water back through the soil and again collect it."

3. Give your children 2 clear quart size jars.

"Label one jar 'rainwater filtered through soil' and the other jar 'plain rainwater'."

"Fill the labeled jars with the appropriate water."

4. Give your children the coleus cutting. They need to be as nearly alike in size as possible.

"These are cuttings from the plant coleus. Describe the properties of the cuttings."

"Choose two that are as nearly alike in size, color, and development as possible."

"Now, put one coleus cutting in the plain rainwater."

"Put another cutting in the jar with rainwater filtered through soil."

"What variable are you testing?"

"What should you do with all the other factors?"

"If the necessary foods come from the soil, which cutting should show the greatest growth and development?"

If the foods come from the rainwater, which plant should do the best or should they do equally well?"

"During the next week or so watch to see what happens."

"Keep careful notes about the properties of the two cuttings."

Each day you must consider ...

"Have you noticed any differences between the plant cuttings? What are some of the differences?"

"What does this experiment lead you to believe about the source of necessary foods for plants."

"Foods are made of specific chemicals. What are the specific chemicals a plant needs to grow as well as to develop new parts?"

5. An extension of this activity would be to test for the affect of specific chemicals on plant growth. A similar experiment was very successful in a large science fair exhibition.

---

4. Look at the container of plant food.

"Look at these three numbers on the front of the label."

"Do you have any idea what they represent?"

"Look at other sections on the label for clues."

Look for the analysis section...

"Find the section titled analysis."

"What chemicals are in the bottle."
(Answer: Check the answer key.)

"What are the per cents of each?"

"Now what do you think the three numbers on the front side of the label represent?"
(Answer: Check the answer key.)

"I wonder how each chemical affects the growth of plants?"

"Design an experiment to test the affect of different chemicals. Use three new plants. They must be as close in size, color, and shape as possible. Coleus or geraniums in water work well.

Test for optimum proportions of chemicals.

"How could you find out the best proportion of these three chemicals on the growth and development of these plants?"

"What factor or variable are you investigating?"
(Answer: Check the answer key.)

"What variables do you need to control?"

As the growth is being observed...

"What is happening to the growth and development of each plant?"

"What effect does each chemical seem to have on the growth and development of these plants?"

ACTIVITY 14
SOIL TYPES AND PLANT GROWTH

MATERIALS
cake pans, 4, disposal, aluminum
dirt
grass seeds
potting soil
rocks, various sizes
weeds

OVERVIEW: EXPANDING THE CONCEPT - ENVIRONMENTAL FACTORS

LESSON PLAN

MATERIALS OR INFORMATION I NEED	WHAT I AM TO DO AND TO CONSIDER
	"You have observed several environmental factors that affect the growth and development of plants." "Do you think the type of soil might be a variable that would affect seed growth?" "Let's make four different trays. In three of the trays you will test soil differences and in the fourth you will test something a little different."
1. Obtain the appropriate materials.	"Fill the first tray with dirt from outside." "Press the dirt together so that if is very firm." "Sprinkle the grass seeds over the top of the soil and water." "Fill another tray with some potting soil, dirt and rocks. Mix them together. Put a few rocks on the top of the soil." "Sprinkle the grass seeds over the top of this soil and water." "Fill the third tray with potting soil." "Sprinkle some grass seeds over the top of this soil and water." "Label the three trays." What variable are you testing? (Answer: Check the answer key.)

"Be sure to keep all the other variables the same during the experiment."

"What do you think will happen in each tray?"

The fourth tray will only work if it is during a time of active weed growth.

"The fourth tray will be a little different."

"Fill it with potting soil."

"Go outside and dig up several weeds by the roots."

"Plant the weeds in the good soil."

"Next, sprinkle some grass seeds over the top of the soil in tray four and then water."

"Be sure that the amount of light, water, and heat are the same for each tray."

"Observe the growth of the grass seeds. Keep a record of the growth."

After the seeds begin to sprout …

"What is beginning to happen?"

"Do you notice any difference in the growth of the seeds?"

"Which tray seems to be the best for growing grass seeds?"

"What environmental factor are you investigating?"

"What do the results tell you?"

2. You can begin ACTIVITY 18 at this time. It is a spiritual application of soil types.

ACTIVITY 15
OTHER EXPERIMENTS WITH PLANTS

MATERIALS
they will depend on the experiments you and your children select

OVERVIEW: EXPANDING THE CONCEPT - ENVIRONMENTAL FACTORS

LESSON PLAN

MATERIALS OR INFORMATION I NEED	WHAT I AM TO DO AND TO CONSIDER
	"You have finished five activities about the environmental factors that affect the growth and development of plants."
	"What are some factors that you have tested?" (Answer: Check the answer key.)
	"What are some variables that you have not tested?" (Answer: Check the answer key.)
	"Do you think the amount of light a plant receives affects its growth and development?" ... What about the temperature of the soil?
Select one or more of the factors yet to be tested. Design an experiment to explore these factors. Tomato, lettuce, or bean seeds work well with these variables.	
Note ... Designing an experiment is difficult to do. Ask your parents for as much help as necessary. Identifying and controlling the variables is essential and also the most difficult. Work patiently. If all the variables are not controlled, it may result it invalid results; however, this can also be a teaching opportunity.	
	"Which factor would you like to explore?"
	"What would you do to test the affect of this variable? ... Design an experiment to test the affect of the variable on the growth of plants. Are you sure that all the other factors are as nearly the same as possible?"

Some suggestions for testing for the amount of light:

Use four pots
Wait about 1 week after planting -

#1 - full light

#2 - cover with a box. Punch holes in the top of the box so that about 75% of the top is full of holes.

#3 - cover with a box. Punch holes in the top of the box so that about 50% of the top is full of holes.

#4 - cover with a box. Punch holes in the top of the box so that about 25% of the top is full of holes.

A variation using four potted plants -
Set a plant in each of the following windows:
a north window, a south window, a west window, and an east window.

ACTIVITY 16
ENVIRONMENTAL FACTORS & ANIMALS

MATERIALS

animals - choose from the following:

      earthworms, 10

      mealworms or adult beetle, 10

      land hermit crabs, 1

soil

thermometer

freeze water in milk carton

trough, a wallpaper hanging plastic tray works great

OVERVIEW: EXPANDING THE CONCEPT -ENVIRONMENTAL FACTORS

LESSON PLAN

MATERIALS OR INFORMATION I NEED	WHAT I AM TO DO AND TO CONSIDER

NOTE TO PARENTS:

This activity allows you to determine your understanding of the following concepts:

Variables, controlling variables, environmental factors, range, optimum range, and experimental design.

"Where do you usually find earthworms? Describe their home, the place where they live."

"The place where an animal normally lives is called its

Habitat."

"How do you think the earthworms would respond to ... moisture? ... Heat? ... Light?"

"Do you think they like wet or dry soil?"

"What about temperature? ... Do you think they would like hot or cold temperatures?"

"Do you think they prefer light or dark?"

"How could you find the answers to these questions?"

THE EFFECT OF HEAT
ON THE MOVEMENT OF EARTHWORMS

"Why is it be important to test for one variable at a time?"
(Answer: Check the answer key.)

"Design an experiment to determine how earth worms respond to temperature?"

"Put one end of the painting trough on the milk carton of ice."

"Set the other end on a heating pad. Be sure the trough is horizontal."

"What variable are you investigating?"

"Make a sketch of the experiment."

"After five minutes take the temperature of the soil in four sections. Record the temperatures on your drawing."

"Place 10 earthworms in the center of the trough."

"Watch the earthworms move. Where are the earthworms in 10 minutes? ... Draw an 'x' to show the location of the 10 earthworms ... Do they prefer hot or cold soil?"

"What was the temperature **range** of the soil in the trough?"

"What was the **optimum** temperature range for the earthworms?"

"Describe how earthworms respond to temperature differences."

3. Now explore the response of earthworms to moisture.

"Now, set up an experiment to see how earthworms respond to moisture."

"What do you think you should do? Design an experiment to test the affect of moisture."

"Make a drawing of your experiment."

3. Finally, explore the response of earthworms to light..

"Finally, set up an experiment to test the response of earthworms to light and dark."

"What should you do? Design an experiment to test the affect of moisture."

"Make a drawing of your experiment.""

"What were the three environmental factors you tested?"

"How did the earthworms respond to each?"

"How would you describe the kind of living environment that earthworms like?"

4. Design and conduct similar experiments using some other animals.

5. Read the mealworm puzzle found on the next page.

"Look at the diagrams."

"What *do* you think? ... What variables are being tested?"

The answer is not only an application of environmental factors but also reasoning abilities. Do not be overly concerned if you have difficulty with this problem.

"Do you think the mealworms respond to light, moisture, to both, or neither? Why do you think so?"

"If you wanted to test just for moisture, how would you set up the experiment?"
(Answer: The box would contain both wet & dry with no light.)

Bill wanted to test the response of mealworms to light and moisture. To do this he set up four boxes as shown in the diagram below. He used lamps for light sources and constantly watered pieces of paper in the boxes for moisture. In the center of each box he placed 20 mealworms. One day later he returned to count the number of mealworms that had crawled to the different ends of the boxes.

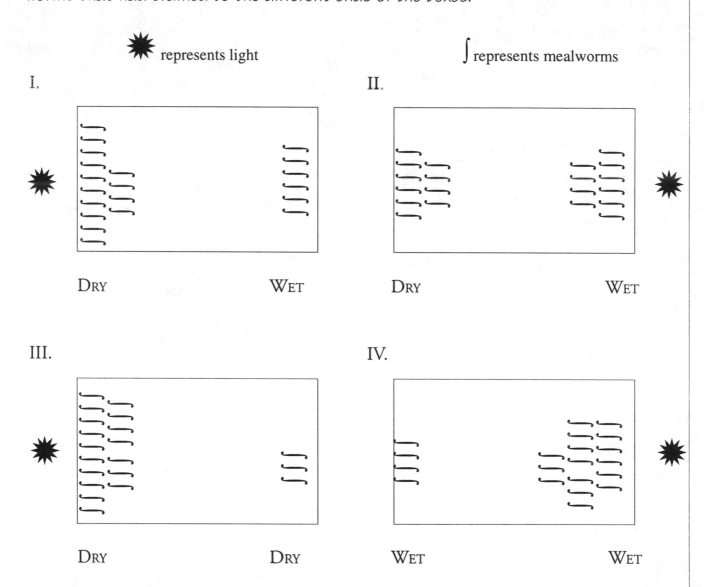

The diagrams show that mealworms move toward or away from:

A) Light but not moisture.
B) Moisture but not light.
C) Both light and moisture.
D) Neither light nor moisture.
Please explain your choice:

ACTIVITY 17
THE GOOD SOIL

MATERIALS
Bible

OVERVIEW: EXPANDING THE CONCEPT - FACTORS

MATERIALS OR INFORMATION I NEED	WHAT I AM TO DO AND TO CONSIDER
Conduct this lesson after you complete Activity 15. 1. Luke 8:4-15; Matthew 13:3-23; Mark 4:1-20.	"Read these verses." "As you read be thinking of questions you may have about these passages of scripture." "What are some questions?" "Tell back as much of the story as you can remember." "Where did the seed fall?" "What affect did each place have on the growth of the seed?" "What is the seed?" "What did the parable mean?" "Which soil do you think represents your live?" "Which soil would you like to have represent your life?"
2. Read Matthew 13:53-58.	"Why couldn't Jesus do many miracles in Nazareth?" "What is faith?"
3. Read Hebrews 11:1. Use a dictionary or thesaurus....	What does this verse say about faith?" "What other words mean the same thing as faith?" "Is God someone you can trust?"

4. Read Titus 1:2.

"What does this tell us about God?"

"Faith is primary in our Christian experience."

5. Read Ephesians 2:8.

"How did you become a Christian?"

6. Read Colossians 2:6.

"How do you walk in the Spirit?"

7. Read Galatians 2:20.

"How does Paul say he lived his life?"

8. Read Galatians 3:1-11.

"What questions do you have about these verses?"

"What do the words **righteousness** and **justified** mean?"

"Why was Abraham righteous?"

"How are you justified?"

"How does a righteous man live?"

"How does God see those who live by faith?"

9. Read Hebrews 11:6.

"What does this verse say about pleasing God?"

"Make a statement about living the Christian life and faith."

Read the selection from the Christian's Secret of a Happy Life.

"For the Christian, who and what are the proper objects of faith?"

10. Read Romans 10:17.

"What does this verse say about faith?"

11. Read mark 11:24.

"What does this verse say about faith?"

The Christian's Secret To A Happy Life
by Hannah Whitall Smith

Faith is very generally misunderstood; for, in reality, faith is the simplest and plainest thing in the world, and the most easy of exercise.

I do beg of you to recognize, then the extreme simplicity of faith; namely, that it is nothing more nor less than just believing God when He says He either has done something for us, or will do it; and then trusting Him to keep His word. It is so simple that it is hard to explain. If anyone asks me what it means to trust another to do a piece of work for me, I can answer only that it means committing the work to that other, and leaving it without anxiety in his hands. All of us have many times trusted very important affairs to others in this way, and have felt perfect rest in thus trusting because of the confidence we have had in those who have undertaken them. How constantly do mothers trust their most precious infants to the care of nurses, and feel no shadow of anxiety! How continually we are all of us trusting our health and our lives, without a thought of fear, to cooks and coachmen, engine-drivers, railway-conductors, and all sorts of paid servants, who have us completely at their mercy, and who could, if they chose to do so, or even if they failed in the necessary carefulness, plunge us into misery or death in a moment. All this we do, and make no demur about it.

You have done this yourself, dear reader, and are doing it continually. You could not live among your fellow men and go through the customary routine of life a single day if you were unable to trust your fellow men, and it never enters into your head to say you cannot. But yet you do not hesitate to say continually, that you cannot trust your God! And you excuse yourself by the plea that you are "a poor weak creature" and "have no faith."

I wish you would try to imagine yourself acting in your human relations as you do in your spiritual relations. Suppose you should begin tomorrow with the notion in your head that you could not trust anybody because you had no faith. When you sat down to breakfast you would say, "I cannot eat anything on this table, for I have no faith, and I cannot believe the cook has not put poison in the coffee, or that the butcher has not sent home diseased or unhealthy meat;" so you would go away starving. When you went out to your daily avocations, you would say, "I cannot ride in the railway train, for I have no faith, and therefore I cannot trust the engineer, nor the conductor, nor the builders of the carriages, nor the managers of the road." And you would be compelled to walk everywhere, and would grow unutterably weary in the effort, besides being actually unable to reach the places you could have reached in the train. When your friends met you with any statements, or your business agent with any accounts, you would say, "I am very sorry that I cannot believe you, but I have no faith, and never can believe anybody."

Just picture such a day as this, and see how disastrous it would be to yourself, and what utter folly it would appear to anyone who should watch you through the whole of it. Realize how your friends would feel insulted, and how your servants would refuse to serve you another day. And then ask yourself the question, if this want of faith in your fellow men would be so dreadful, and such utter folly, what must it be when you tell God that you have no power to trust Him, nor to believe His word; that it is a great trial, but you cannot help it, "for you have no faith."

Remember always that there are two things which are more utterly incompatible even than oil and water, and these two are trust and worry. Would you call it trust if you should give something into the hands of a friend to attend to for you, and then should spend your nights and days in anxious thought and worry as to whether it would be rightly and successfully done? And can you call it trust, when you have given the saving and keeping of your soul into the hands of the Lord, if day after day, and night after night, you are spending hours of anxious thought and questioning about the matter? When a believer really trusts anything, he ceases to worry about the thing he has trusted. And when he worries, it is a plain proof that he does not trust. Tested by this rule, how little real trust there is in the Church of Christ! No wonder our Lord asked the pathetic question, "When the Son of man cometh, shall he find faith on the earth?"

You have trusted Him in a few things, and He has not failed you. Trust Him now for everything, and see if He does not do for you exceedingly abundantly, above all that you could ever have asked or even thought, not according to your power or capacity, but according to His own mighty power, working in you all the good pleasure of His most blessed will.

It is not hard, you find, to trust the management of the universe, and of all the outward creation, to the Lord. Can your case then be so much more complex and difficult that these, that you need to be anxious or troubled about His management of you? Away with such unworthy doubtings! Take your stand on the power and trustworthiness of your God, and see how quickly all difficulties will vanish before a steadfast determination to believe. Trust in the dark, trust in the light, trust at night and trust in the morning, and you will find that the faith that many begin, perhaps by a mighty effort will end, sooner or later, be becoming the easy and natural habit of the soul. It is a law of the spiritual life that every act of trust makes the next act less difficult, until at length, if these acts are persisted in, trusting becomes, like breathing, the natural unconscious action of the redeemed soul.

Let your faith, then, "throw its arms around all God has told you," and in every dark hour remember that "though now for a season, if need be, ye are in heaviness through manifold temptations," it is only like going through a tunnel. The sun has not ceased shining because the traveler through the tunnel has ceased to see it; and the Son of righteousness is still shining, although you in your dark tunnel do not see Him. Be patient and trustful, and wait. This time of darkness is only permitted that "the trial of your faith, being much more precious than of gold that perisheth, though it be tried with fire, might be found unto praise and honor and glory at the appearing of Jesus Christ."

ACTIVITY 18
AIRPLANES

MATERIALS
typing paper

OVERVIEW: EXPLORING THE CONCEPT - ENERGY

LESSON PLAN

MATERIALS OR INFORMATION I NEED	WHAT I AM TO DO AND TO CONSIDER
1. This is a fun family activity. Include everyone in your family. The library has books on paper airplanes that might be of interest.	"Design the best paper airplane you can."
	"Now, test your design by flying the airplane."
Note: After completing this activity you might like to build balsa wood gliders or Estess Rockets. Contact your local hobby shop for details.	"See if you can improve the flight of your airplane. Be sure to keep a careful record of exactly how you designed your paper plane."
2. Plan a paper airplane flying contest.	"Let's have a paper airplane flying contest."
	CONTEST #1 "The winner of the first contest will be the airplane that flies the farthest."
	"You can fold the plane any way you wish, but you can not add anything to it."
	"Make a couple of test flights."
When every one is ready …	"Now, you will fly one plane at a time. The plane that goes the farthest is the winner."
After the contest …	"Examine the winning airplane closely."
	"Compare the winning airplane with your plane. How does the winning airplane differ from yours?"
	"Make a record of those differences."

When everyone is ready ...

Contest #2
"The winning plane for the second contest will be the plane which flies the highest."

"Test fly your plane when you are ready."

'Okay, let's see which plane will fly the highest."

"Which airplane wins this contest?"

"Examine the winner closely and compare it with your plane."

"How are they alike? ... Different?"

"There are variables among the paper airplanes. What variables do you observe?"

"Select the three variables that you feel have the most effect on your paper airplane system.."

"Design an experiment to test each variable. How can you be sure that you are testing the variable you want to test? Design a plan before starting the experiment."

After the testing ...

"Which variables did you investigate?"

"Which variable is the most important? Did you keep all variables except one the same?"

Contest #3
"The winning plane in this final contest is the one which turns the most to the left or to the right. Everyone must throw their plane straight ahead. The one which makes the sharpest turn wins this contest."

"Okay, design your plane and test your design. When everyone is ready the contest will begin."

"It is time to begin the contest. Everyone throw your plane."

"Which airplane wins this contest?"

"Examine the winner closely and compare it to your plane."

"How are they alike? ... How are they different? Make any modifications to your plane and repeat this contest."

ACTIVITY 19
SLINGSHOT SYSTEM

MATERIALS
slingshot
rubber bands of different sizes and thicknesses
marbles

OVERVIEW: EXPLORING THE CONCEPT - ENERGY

LESSON PLAN

MATERIALS OR INFORMATION I NEED	WHAT I AM TO DO AND TO CONSIDER
NOTE TO PARENTS: Provide close supervision during this activity. Children must NEVER aim a slingshot at any person or animal. If your children will not follow this rule, then omit this activity. 1. Obtain a handful of different kinds of rubber bands.	"Describe the properties of these objects." "How are they alike? ... Different?" "What is the one thing that they all have in common?" "Use your dictionary to find the meaning of the word 'elastic' and make a record of the meaning." "Make a list of as many elastic systems as you can think of."
2. Help your children make a slingshot.	"A slingshot is an elastic system. "
3. Obtain several marbles. Each marble should be the same shape and size.	"Use each rubber band as a slingshot. Shoot a marble from each rubber-band slingshot. Find out which rubber band will shoot a marble the farthest." "Be sure the marble you shoot is not a variable in your experiment. What must you do to keep the marble from being a variable?" "What other variables must you keep the same?" "What is the variable in this experiment?"

"Study the rubber band and list all its properties. Each property may help the rubber band to shoot a marble."

"How could you test the property of the length of the rubber band?"
(Answer: Check the answer key.)

"How could you test the property of width of the rubber band?"
(Answer: Check the answer key.)

"How could you test for stretching?"

"Design an experiment to test each property. When you test a property for its effect on shooting distances, what has the property become?"
(Answer: Check the answer key.)

"Using a measuring tape determine the distance of each marble. Be sure to keep accurate records of your investigation."

"Which rubber band shoots a marble the farthest?"

"Which property is the most helpful?"

ACTIVITY 20
MELTING ICE

MATERIALS
cake pan
glass containers, 4
ice
metal fruit juice can
Styrofoam cup
thermometer
water

OVERVIEW: EXPLORING THE CONCEPT - ENERGY

LESSON PLAN

MATERIALS OR INFORMATION I NEED	WHAT I AM TO DO AND TO CONSIDER
1. Obtain the necessary materials.	"Place four ice cubes in the cake pan and four ice cubes into a glass filled with water. Record the time."
	"Predict which group of ice cubes you think will melt first? ... Why do you think so?"
Just before all the ice is melted ...	"How cold do you think the water is now? Stir the water and measure the temperature now."
	"How long did it take for the ice cubes in each container to melt?"
	"Is it what you had expected?"
	"Explain why you believe the melting times were different for the ice in the water and the ice in the air.
	"What was the temperature of the water just before the ice disappeared?"
	"This temperature is important. The ice melted at this temperature. What would be a good name for this temperature?"
(Answer: Check the answer key.)

2. This portion of the activity is fun for the whole family.. Encourage your whole family to participate.

Give each person an ice cube of the same size and a container to collect the water.

"Each member of your family has an ice cube and a container. The ice cubes should all be about the same size."

"For a period of one minute, do anything you wish to melt your ice cube. The person having the most water at the end of one minute wins."

"Ready! Set! Go!"

At the end of one minute ...

"Now, measure the amount of water each person has collected."

"Who has the most water?"

"What method did you use to melt the ice cube?"

"What were the variables in this experiment?"

"How did each variable make the ice melt?"

"Make a list of the actions you observed."

"Why do you think each action melts ice?"

3. This portion of the activity deals with several special problems.

"Get three ice cubes which are the same size."

"Put one in a fruit-juice can, another in a glass container, and the third one in a styrofoam cup. Cover the containers with clear plastic wrap."

"Will the ice from each container melt at the same time? ... Which do you think will melt first? ...Second? ...Last?"

"Observe the action."

"Which ice cubes melted first? ...Last?"

"Is that what you had expected?"

"Explain why they melted in the order that they did."

"A material can be used to keep heat from moving from one place to another. The material blocks the flow of heat. Such a material is known as

Insulation.

How does insulation help to explain what you observed in the experiment?"

"Name some places that insulation is used ... Tell why it helps."

3. You will need three glasses of the same size.

"Put one ice cube in one of the glass containers ... Put two ice cubes in the second glass container ... And completely fill the third glass with ice cubes."

"Now, put as much water as you can in each glass."

"Measure the temperature of the water in each glass every five minutes. Stir the water occasionally. Keep a record of your data."

"What was the lowest temperature of the water ?"

"How much time did it take for the water to reach the lowest temperature."

"The temperature and the measurement of time are quantitative data. Make a graph of these results."

"Look at the graph. What is the lowest temperature which the water in each glass reached?"

"What was the condition of the ice when the water reached the lowest temperature?"

"What had to happen to the ice-water system before the temperature started to rise from its lowest reading?"

"In which ice-water system did the temperature remain the same the longest?"

"When the lowest temperature was reached and ice was still in the system, what was the temperature?"

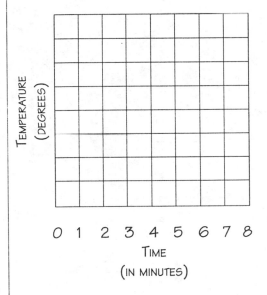

TEMPERATURE (DEGREES)

0 1 2 3 4 5 6 7 8

TIME

(IN MINUTES)

ACTIVITY 21
SLOPES

MATERIALS
books, several
cardboard, 24 inches, to make a ramp
eraser
nuts, large, metal
ruler
balls, golf ball, baseball and softball
tape

OVERVIEW: NAMING THE CONCEPT - ENERGY

LESSON PLAN

MATERIALS OR INFORMATION I NEED	WHAT I AM TO DO AND TO CONSIDER
1. Go to a location that has both steps and a ramp.	"Walk up the sloping walk."
	"Now, walk up the flight of stairs."
	"Which is easier to climb, the slope or the steps."
	"A sloping walkway or a sloping roadway is a ramp. One end of a ramp is always higher than the other end. Another name for a ramp is an **inclined plane.**"
	"Use the dictionary to find out what the words **'inclined'** and **'plane'** mean."
	"Why is 'inclined plane' a suitable name for a ramp?"
	"An inclined plane is one of the most basic machines known. It is called a **simple machine.**"
2. You will need the materials listed above.	"For your first experiment you will need three balls. A golf ball, a baseball, and a softball will do."
	"Using the books and cardboard, make a ramp that is about ten centimeters higher on one end than the other."
	"Next, you will need a chalkboard eraser. Set the eraser at the lower end of the ramp."

"Then roll the spheres down the ramp and into the eraser. Set the eraser so that the spheres hit it squarely when they come off the ramp. Practice with your set up until it works just right."

"Now, you are ready to do the experiment."

"Roll each of the balls into the eraser. Measure and make a record of the distances which the spheres push the eraser ... Your record will consist of quantitative data.

"Which ball pushed the eraser farthest?

"Now, raise the higher end of the ramp about five centimeters."

"Do the experiment again ... Keep track of the distances.

"Which ball pushed the eraser the farthest."

"Raise the end another five centimeters and do the experiment again."

"Which ball pushed the erase the farthest?"

"At which ramp height did the eraser go the farthest?"

"Make a statement about raising the ramp and the distance the eraser is pushed."

"Why do you think it has that affect?"

---

3. You will need the tape and three metal nuts.

"Now, I want you to change the experiment a little."

"In this experiment use the ball that pushed the eraser the farthest."

"Keep the ramp at one height. Keep it at the height at which the eraser moved the farthest. Measure how far the eraser moves each time."

"Fasten one weight to the eraser."

"Then roll the ball down the ramp."

"How far does the eraser go?"

"Fasten two weights to the eraser. Then repeat the experiment."

"Finally, repeat the experiment with three weights."

DISTANCE

WEIGHTS

The idea -

"Make a bar graph to represent your data."

"What can you conclude from this experiment?"

"How can the eraser be pushed the farthest?"

"How far do you think the eraser would go if it had four weights on it?"

"Make a statement that relates the weight of the ball, the height of the ramp, the weight of the eraser and the distance the eraser."

"Now, review what your experiments have told you about action:

• A person has to throw a paper airplane to make it go.

• A rubber band has to be stretched before it can shoot an object.

• When ice is put in water, the ice melts and the water gets cold.

• The greater the weight from which a ball rolls down a ramp, the farther it will push an eraser.

The experiments you have done produced the results they did because of

Energy."

"The person gives the airplane energy when throwing it."

"The rubber band gains energy when it is stretched."

"Ice gains energy from the water and melts."

"The ball gains energy by rolling down the inclined plane."

"When the ball strikes the eraser, it gives the eraser energy."

"The system giving the energy is the

Energy source."

The system receiving the energy is the

Energy receiver."

"Think back upon the experiments in this section. What was the energy source in each experiment? ... What was the energy receiver?"

"What kind of energy causes ice to melt?"

"What is the energy source for a moving automobile?"

"During the week look for evidence of energy sources and energy receivers."

4. Begin activity 34: The Power of God at this time.

ACTIVITY 22
PLAY BALL!

MATERIALS
baseball equipment, ball, bat, and gloves

OVERVIEW: EXPANDING THE CONCEPT - ENERGY

LESSON PLAN

MATERIALS OR INFORMATION I NEED	WHAT I AM TO DO AND TO CONSIDER
Go to a park where you and your family can play baseball. Ask your mom to pack a picnic lunch!	"As you now have observed, energy makes it possible for a paper airplane to fly and sail through the air. A rubber band has energy when it stretches and snaps back." "There are many everyday examples of energy and of how energy plays an important part in your daily activities. Wherever you are you can observe energy in action."
1. You will need a baseball, bat, and gloves. After you have played for several minutes ...	"Let's go outside and play baseball." "Describe what is happening using the words — **energy, energy source,** & **energy receiver.**" "This is an example of energy in action. The pitcher has energy when he winds up and throws the ball. The ball itself has energy when it streaks toward the plate. The bat has energy when it is being swung. As the ball sails away, it still has energy. The man in center field has energy, too. He uses energy to run, catch the ball, and throw it back in." "As you have learned from doing experiments, an object receives energy from a source." "The ball receives energy from the bat. The bat receives energy from the batter. Batter ————> bat ————> ball "This diagram is read ' **the batter gives energy to the bat and the bat gives energy to the ball.**'"

"First, one object receives energy. Then it gives energy to another receiver. There is an exchange of energy. You can observe many exchanges of energy in the happenings around you."

HAVE FUN PLAYING BALL!

"After you come home from playing ball, draw several other diagrams showing the transfer of energy.

ACTIVITY 23
ENERGY CHAINS

MATERIALS
bicycles
pan
range top
water

OVERVIEW: EXPANDING THE CONCEPT - ENERGY

LESSON PLAN

MATERIALS OR INFORMATION I NEED	WHAT I AM TO DO AND TO CONSIDER
	WIND ————> SAIL ————> BOAT
	"Read this diagram."
	"Name the energy sources and energy receivers."
1. You will need the materials listed above. . Because you will be using a heat source, **ask your parents for assistance!**	
	"Pour a small amount of water into the pan. Now put the pan on the range top."
	"Observe what happens."
	"What happened to the water? Is it gone. This is called **evaporation**."
	Stove top ————> water ————> air
	"Read this diagram ... Name the energy sources ... Energy receivers."
	"What does it mean?"
The idea	
	"One object or system giving energy to another object or system is evidence of
	Energy transfer.
	A diagrams like the ones above are called an
	Energy chain.

An energy chain tells you how the energy in a system is moving from the source to the receiver."

2. Go outside and ride your bikes ...

"As you ride your bike, think about energy source, energy receiver, energy transfer, and energy chain."

After you finish riding your bikes ...

"Draw a diagram that represents the energy chain as you ride your bike."
(Answer: Check the answer key.)

"What evidence of energy transfer do you have?"
(Answer: Check the answer key.)

Be on the lookout for these concepts in your everyday living. Draw the energy chain for some of their observations.

"During the next couple of days look for some everyday examples of energy transfer ... Make a diagram showing the appropriate energy chains of at least five such chains."

ACTIVITY 24
TEMPERATURE BALANCE

MATERIALS
birthday candle
clothespins, 2
food coloring
glass container, 1 large, 1 small
hole punch
measuring cup, liquid
pebble
pill-bottle with cap, a 35mm film cannister will also work
quart jar, 1, wide mouth ,
cans, 2 small
Styrofoam cup, large
thermometer

OVERVIEW: EXPANDING THE CONCEPT - ENERGY

LESSON PLAN

MATERIALS OR INFORMATION I NEED	WHAT I AM TO DO AND TO CONSIDER
NOTE TO PARENTS: This activity involves using hot water and a heat source. Provide adequate supervision to insure the safety of your children. It will take several sessions to complete all the experiments.	
1. You will need the measuring cup, 1 large glass, 1 small glass, and the thermometer.	"Put 1/2 cup of tap water in large glass container." "Put 1/2 cup of water heated to about 80 ℃ in a smaller container.." "Record the temperature of the water in each container." "Then place the small container in the large container." "Measure the temperature of the water in each container every minute for twenty minutes."

You will need graph paper.

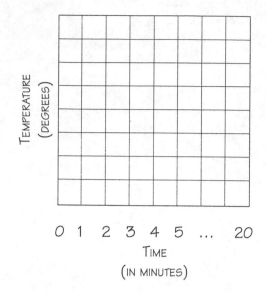

TEMPERATURE (DEGREES)

0   1   2   3   4   5   ...   20

TIME

(IN MINUTES)

"Graph the temperature and time on the graph. Plot the time-temperature curve for both sets of data on the same graph."

"Describe what happened?"

"What are the energy sources and the energy receivers?"

"What evidence do you have that energy has been transferred?"

"What do you think the temperature of the water will be after two hours?"

"What will the data you collected permit you to say about how heat moves from one object to another?"

"Heat is sometimes called

Thermal energy."

2. You will need 1 wide mouth jar, the pill-bottle with cap, hole punch, pebble, and food coloring.

"Punch two small holes in a plastic pill-bottle cap."

"Put the small pebble and eight or ten drops of food coloring into the plastic pill bottle."

"Fill the large jar with tap water. Measure the temperature. Fill the pill bottle with very hot water."

"Place the cap on the pill bottle."

"Then place the bottle in the large jar."

"After two or three minutes, carefully measure the temperature of the water at the top of the jar ... Also measure the temperature at the bottom." (Answer: Check the answer key)

"Describe how warm water moves in cool water ... What evidence do you have?"

"How is the smoke from a smokestack like what you just observed in this experiment?"

"How is the energy in the experiment transferred from one place to another?"

"What is your evidence of energy transfer."

3. You will need 2 clothespins, a birthday candle, and a small can.

"Place 1/4 cup of water in a small can."

"Use the thermometer to measure the temperature of the cold water."

Note to parents:
Provide assistance to insure safety.

"Then hold the can containing the water over a flaming birthday candle for one minute

"Use the clothespins to hold the can and the candle."

"Heat the water for one minute and then measure the temperature of the water."

"What is the change in temperature?"

"What is the energy source?"

"What is the energy receiver?"

"What is the evidence of energy transfer?"

"Draw the energy chain for this system."

---

4. You will need two small cans.

"Next, use two small cans."

"Place 1/4 cup of water in each can."

"Measure the temperature of the water "

"Heat the water in one can until it is about 70 °C."

"Pour the warm water into the cool water in the other can."

"Measure the temperature of the mixed water."

"What is the energy source?"

"What is the energy receiver?"

"What is the evidence of energy transfer?"

"Draw the diagram that show the energy chain."

"Thermal energy is measured in calories (c). A kilocalorie (c) is 1,000 calories."

5. You will need another piece of graph paper.

Experiments from step 5 & 6 should be conducted on the same day.

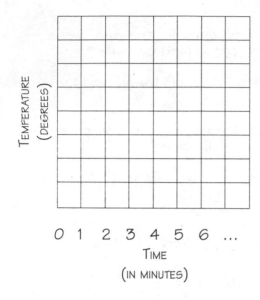

"Pour 1/4 cup of water into a small can and record the temperature."

"Heat the water to a temperature of 60 ℃."

"After the water is heated, measure its temperature every three minutes. Measure the temperature ten times."

"You are to observe the change in temperature over time."

"Make a graph of your data. What part of the graph will you use for each variable?"

"How long will it take for the water to have the same temperature it had before it was heated? What will happen then?"

"What were the energy sources in this experiment? ...What were the energy receivers?"

"Draw the energy chain showing the energy transfer."

6. You will need a small can and a large styrofoam cup.

"Pour 1/4 cup of water into a small can and record the temperature."

"Heat the water in the can to a temperature of 60 ℃."

"Next, put the can containing the water into a styrofoam cup."

"Place a lid over the cup."

"Take the temperature of the water every three minutes until you have taken three readings."

"Graph the data."

"How long will it take for the water to become the same temperature it was before you heated it?"

"Describe how the energy transfer was different in the last two experiments."

"Make a statement that describes what happens when liquids of different temperatures are put together."

The idea -

"The temperature they end up with is greater than the cold one you started with and less than the warmer one you started with."

"One temperature of one liquid decreased while the temperature of other liquid increased. The temperature of the two liquids came to a balance when they were put together. That balanced temperature is between the temperatures of the two liquids. The temperature which the combined liquids come to is an

Equilibrium temperature."

The word 'equilibrium' means balanced or equal. When two liquids of different temperatures are put together, their temperatures reach an equilibrium temperature."

"Draw the energy chain showing the energy transfer from hot to cold water."
(Answer: Hot water ——> cold water)

---

7. You will need 2 glasses -
one large glass, one small glass.

"Put some very cold water in a large glass and measure its temperature."

"Next, put some warm water in the small glass and measure its temperature."

"If you mix the water from the two glasses together what do you think the temperature will become?"

"Now, mix the two amounts of water together and measure the temperature of the mixture of warm and cold water ... Is it what you had expected?"

"What can you say about the equilibrium temperature?"

"Is there a way to predict the final temperature of water to be mixed, if you know the initial temperature of the two containers of water?"

8. You will need the measuring cup and a large glass.

"Put exactly 1/4 cup of water in a large glass and measure its temperature."

"Heat some water and measure its temperature."

"What do you think the equilibrium temperature will be, if the cold and hot water are mixed? Do you think it matters how hot the water is? Does it matter how much of the hot and cold water are mixed?"

"Put exactly 1/4 cup of the hot water with the cooler water?"

"Measure the temperature of the combined liquids. Is it what you had expected?"

"Make a statement relating equilibrium temperature and mixing **equal** amounts of water."

"Repeat this experiment using 1/2 cup of cold water and, 1 cup of warm water. "

"If the amounts of initial water are not the same, what effect does that have on the final temperature?"

"Try several other combinations of liquid amounts to test your idea."

"Make a statement about equilibrium temperature and mixing equal and unequal amounts of water"

9. These are some questions that will help you evaluate your understanding.

"If you were to mix one gallon of water at 40°C with one gallon of water at 90°C, what would the equilibrium temperature be?"

"Your body's temperature is about 37 °C. You put your hand in water having a temperature of 10 °C. Which is the energy source? Which is the energy receiver? What affect will there be on the water?"

10. To expand this activity use equal and unequal amounts of different liquids - for example, corn oil and water. You may need to ask your parents for help.

"What do you think the equilibrium temperature will be if you use equal amounts of two different liquids?"

"Design and conduct an experiment to test your prediction."

"Is that what you expected? ...Does the kind of material seem to affect equilibrium temperature?"

11. Read the story of Goldilocks and the three bears.

"What do you think about the three bowls of porridge?"

"It said that the large bowl was too hot ... The medium bowl was too cold... And the small bowl was just right."

"Assuming that the porridge was the same for each bowl and that it was poured at the same time, is it possible that the small bowl could be at a temperature between the large and small bowl?"

"Explain your answer."

"Design an experiment to test this part of the goldilocks story?"

"How many bowls will you need? The starting temperature for each of the three bowls should be the same.

"Take the temperature of the three bowls of porridge (soup) every minute for ten minutes."

"Make a chart showing the results."

"Using different colored pens make a graph showing the change in temperature for each bowl size. The graphs of each bowl should be on the same graph paper."

"What do you conclude about the temperature of the small bowl? Could it have been 'just right'?"

ACTIVITY 25
PASSING THROUGH?

MATERIALS
aluminum foil
BB's
candle
clothes hanger
cooking oil
pan
popsicle stick
thermometer
white syrup

OVERVIEW: EXPANDING THE CONCEPT - ENERGY

LESSON PLAN

MATERIALS OR INFORMATION I NEED   WHAT I AM TO DO AND TO CONSIDER

NOTE TO PARENTS:
This activity involves the use of heat and a candle. Provide close supervision at all times.

1. You will need the clothes hanger, candle, and bb's.

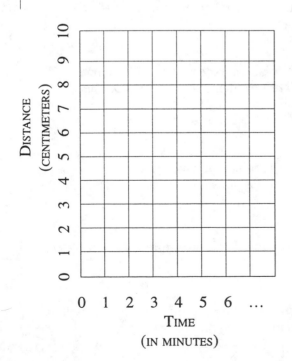

Distance (Centimeters) vs. Time (in minutes)

"For this experiment the clothes hanger can be left in its original shape. You can use the neck of the hanger as a handle. Put ten drops of candle wax one centimeter apart on the long section of the hanger."

"Wait until the drops of wax are almost solid. Then push a 'bb' into each spot of wax."

"Next, place a burning candle under one end of the wire."

"Measure how many seconds it takes for each bb to drop from the wax."

"Make a graph of your data."

"What is the evidence that energy was transferred through the metal rod."

"How does the energy transfer change as it moves along the rod?"

The idea -

"As you have observed, heat can move through a metal rod. The transfer of energy through a material such as a metal rod is called

Conduction."

"The material which allows the energy to be transferred through it is called a

Conductor."

"What action did conduction produce in the coat hanger experiment?"

"Conduction is a passing through. For example, there is conduction when water passes through a pipe. Water is transferred from a large tank to your home through pipes. The water moves from one place to another through the pipe. The hollow pipe is a conductor. It is a conductor of water."

"A solid piece of copper or iron will not allow water or gas to pass through it. Solids are not conductors of liquids and gases. But a solid piece of metal will let some things pass through. Heat and electricity can pass through solid metal."

"Some materials do not let heat and electricity pass through. Such materials block the flow of heat and electricity, just as a solid metal blocks the flow of water. For example, asbestos allows only a very little heat energy to pass through it. Glass will not allow electricity to pass through. Materials which do not conduct electricity or heat are called

Nonconductors."

"Now you will do some experiments in which you will test how well different materials conduct heat. The material itself is the only variable you will be testing. Be sure to keep everything else in the experiments the same."

"In the first experiment you will be working with a piece of wood and a piece of metal."

2. You will need a popsicle stick, aluminum foil, a thermometer, and a pan.

"Touch a thermometer to one end of the popsicle stick and the aluminum foil. Record the temperature."

"Heat the other end by putting them into a pan of water and then heating the water."

"Measure how long it takes for the thermometer to show a change in temperature for each item.."

"Which material is the better conductor? ... What is your evidence?"

---

3. You will need a thermometer, a pan, cooking oil and white syrup.

"Put 1/2 cup of water in the pan."

"Hang the thermometer in the water so that only the bulb is completely covered. What is the temperature?"

Use low heat.
Be careful whenever using heat!

"Heat the pan and water for one minute."

"Record the temperature at the end of the one minute."

You will need to wait for the pan to cool to room temperature.

"Clean out the pan."

"Next, pour 1/2 cup of cooking oil into the pan."

"Hang the thermometer in the cooking oil so that only the bulb is completely covered. What is the temperature?"

"Heat the pan and oil for one minute."

"Record the temperature at the end of the one minute."

You will need to wait for the pan to cool to room temperature.

"Clean out the pan."

"Next, pour 1/2 cup of white syrup into the pan."

"Hang the thermometer in the white syrup so that only the bulb is completely covered. What is the temperature?"

"Heat the pan and syrup for one minute."

"Record the temperature at the end of the one minute."

"Which liquid is the best conductor of heat? ... What is your evidence?"

"Which is the better conductor of heat a solid or a liquid? ... What is your evidence?"

ACTIVITY 26
ON HOLD

MATERIALS
candle
clothes hanger
corn flakes
dried bread
matches
play-doh
quart jar
rockets, ESTES model
shredded wheat

OVERVIEW: EXPANDING THE CONCEPT - ENERGY

LESSON PLAN

MATERIALS OR INFORMATION I NEED	WHAT I AM TO DO AND TO CONSIDER
1. Give your children the birthday candle, play-doh, matches and a quart jar.	"Set an unlit birthday candle into some play-doh."
	"Examine the unlit candle."
	"Is energy transfer happening?"
	"How could it be used as an energy source?"
Parents, provide close supervision!	"Now, light the candle with a match."
	"Carefully hold your hand above the flaming candle."
	"How do you know energy is being transferred?" (Answer: Check the answer key.)
	"Watch the candle for several minutes."
	"In what way is the candle changing."
	"Place a quart-sized jar over the burning candle and observe what happens."
	"Is the candle still burning? ... Is energy being transferred?"

The idea -

"When the candle burned, its wick and wax disappeared. The burning candle gave up heat energy."

"The candle wax was the source of

Stored Energy.

"Another name for stored energy is

Potential Energy.

"Before being lighted the candle had the potential to be an energy source. Potential energy is energy that is stored or that is on hold for use at a later time."

"Potential energy can be stored in an object when it is raised above the earth. The object has energy because, if it is released, it will fall back to the earth. To move, an object must have energy."

"When the stored potential energy is released the object moves. The energy of motion is called

Kinetic energy."

"A compressed spring has potential energy. If it is released, the spring will uncoil, or move back to its original position. The spring can push or pull on another object as it moves."

2. Hold the following items over your sink with a pair of tongs:
shredded wheat, a piece of dried bread, and a sugar corn flake (or other similar items).

"Hold a lighted match to each piece of food."

"Describe what happens."

"How is food like the candle?"

"What do these results tell you about food and energy?"
(Answer: Check the answer key.)

"What sources of potential energy do you depend upon from day to day?"

"Name three different materials which contain potential energy."

3. Flying balsa gliders or launching Estess model rockets are creative ways to demonstrate potential and kinetic energy. Ask your parents about the possibility of going to your local hobby shop to purchase either an Estess model rocket or a balsa glider.

ACTIVITY 27
CHANGE

MATERIALS
aluminum pan, 2
baking soda
glass containers, 2
measuring cup, liquid
pan, 2
teaspoon
tongs
vinegar

OVERVIEW: EXPANDING THE CONCEPT - ENERGY

LESSON PLAN

MATERIALS OR INFORMATION I NEED	WHAT I AM TO DO AND TO CONSIDER
1. You will need the materials listed above..	"Put 50 ml of white vinegar in one clear glass.
	"In a second clear glass put 50 ml of water."
	"Now, add 1 teaspoonful of baking soda to each glass. Add the baking soda a little at a time."
	"Stir slowly and carefully."
	"Observe the action in each system. When all action has stopped in each system, let the two systems set for a few minutes."
	"Call the vinegar-soda system 'System V' and the water-soda system 'System W'."
	"How are 'System V' and 'System W' different? Explain the differences by describing the properties of the two systems."
	"Get two large pans. Put 200 ml of water in each pan."
	"Next, put the liquid from 'System V' into a small aluminum pan."
	"Put the liquid from 'System W' into a second aluminum pan."

"Then float one pan on the water in one pan. Float the other pan on the water in the second pan."

NOTE TO PARENTS:
Always provide close supervision around heat sources.

"Now, put the pans on the range top."

"Heat the water filled pans which have the aluminum pans floating on the water. Heat the pans until all the material in the aluminum pans is boiled away."

"Using a pair of tongs carefully remove the aluminum pans from the hot water."

Let the materials dry and cool."

"Observe the material that is left in each aluminum pan."

"Compare the material that came from 'System V' with the material from 'System W'."

"How are the two materials alike?:"

"How are they different?"

"Make a record of the properties of each system."

"Squeeze each solid material between your fingers ... What properties do you observe?"

"You started the experiment with baking soda. Compare the properties of baking soda with the material from 'System W' and the material from 'System V'."

"Which of these materials has properties like the properties of baking soda?"

"To test how the materials from 'System V' and 'System W' compare with baking soda, grind up the materials from each system. Feel the powder from each. Feel the baking soda."

"Very carefully taste a small amount of each of the materials. These materials will not harm you."

"As a general rule, **never** taste anything from an experiment unless you are sure it will not harm you."

"Do both of the materials taste like baking soda?"

The idea -

"In one of the systems the properties of the soda did not change. In the other system the properties of soda changed. One of the systems returned soda. The other system did not. Whenever the properties of a material are changed in a system, a

Chemical Change has taken place.

The looks of a piece of matter can be changed, but the material is the same. When that happens, a

Physical Change has taken place."

"A physical change can be a simple change. For example, crushing a piece of ice is a physical change. Cutting a piece of paper into shreds is a physical change. A physical change does not change what the object is made of."

"Sometimes a **physical change** makes an object look different. For example, you can change the looks of an object by heating it. The object melts or boils. But, if you take the heat away, the object cools. The material changes back to the way it first looked. It is still the same material."

A **chemical change** is a drastic change. It is a change into a different material. When a candle burns, you cannot get it back by cooling the wax and gases. The original materials no longer exist. In their place are new and different materials."

"What is one difference between a physical change and a chemical change?"

"What happens when a substance undergoes a chemical change?"

"How could you make a physical change in water?"

"Is the melting of ice a physical change or a chemical change?"

"What kind of change occurs when an egg is cooked?"

"During the week be on the look for examples **physical** and **chemical changes**."

ACTIVITY 28
THE INSIDE STORY

MATERIALS
beans, bush and lima 25 each
peanut butter jar, plastic
paper towels

OVERVIEW: EXPLORING THE CONCEPT - PHOTOSYNTHESIS

LESSON PLAN

MATERIALS OR INFORMATION I NEED	WHAT I AM TO DO AND TO CONSIDER
1. The day before beginning this activity: In separate pans soak about 25 bush beans and 25 lima beans.	
2. Set the soaked seeds on two paper towels.	"Observe the outside of these seeds." "What do you think is inside a seed? Do you think it is hollow or solid?" "Do you think that the inside of one type of seed is the same or different from another type?" "Carefully split several seeds lengthwise along the middle with your fingernails." "Compare what you see inside the seed with the picture." "This is the **seed coat**." "This is the **cotyledon** [kaht uhl eed uhnz)" "This part is called the **embryo**." "What do you think the purpose of each part to the plant might be?" "How could you design an experiment to see the purpose of the embryo and cotyledon?" "Germinate the embryo and the cotyledon separately." "Also germinate the embryo with one cotyledon."

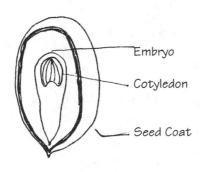

Embryo

Cotyledon

Seed Coat

If you are not sure what germinate means, look it up in a dictionary.

"Finally, you will germinate the embryo with both cotyledons - the complete bean seed."

---

3. You will need a plastic peanut butter jar and a paper towel.

"Poke four holes in the bottom of the peanut butter jar. Set the paper towel in the lid and wet it."

Care must be taken in separating the parts. You should use new bean seeds for this part of the activity.

"Place the four parts of the bean seed on the paper towel."

"Screw the jar onto the lid."

"Set the germination system in a lighted area but not in direct sunlight."

If you see mold growing in the system remove the jar for several hours so that it can dry out.

"Water the system every other day."

"Observe the parts over the next 2 weeks."

During the 2 week period...

"Do you see anything happening to any of the parts?"

"Which seed parts are growing ? Which seed parts are not growing?"

"Which combinations of parts are growing? Which is growing the best - the whole seed or the half?"

At the conclusion ...

"Why do think the embryo and cotyledon do not grow separately but grow when they are combined?"

The next questions are for thought....

"I wonder, what is the purpose of the embryo?"

"And what is the purpose of the cotyledon?"

ACTIVITY 29
PHOTO WHAT?

MATERIALS
fertilizer, plant food, (optional)
grass seeds
planter cups, 4
potting soil
ruler

OVERVIEW: NAMING THE CONCEPT - PHOTOSYNTHESIS

LESSON PLAN

MATERIALS OR INFORMATION I NEED	WHAT I AM TO DO AND TO CONSIDER
	"What do plants need in order to grow? Do you think plants need light to grow? ... Why do you think so?"
1. You will need the materials listed above..	"Put soil into the four cups."
	"Sprinkle the grass seeds on the surface of each and then cover these with a thin layer of soil."
	"Water the soil until it is moist."
	"In this experiment you will keep everything the same except the amount of light."
	"What variable are you investigating?" (Answer: Check the answer key.)
	"What should you do to determine if plants need light to grow?"
	"Right! You should set two cups in a dark place and the other two need to be set in indirect sunlight."
	"Write 'dark' on these and 'light' on the others "
Water every second or third day...	"Keep the soil of both planters equally moist - but not too wet."
	"What do you think will happen to the seeds in each planter? ... Why do you think so?"
	"Do you think the seeds in the dark will grow at all? ... Why or why not?"

"Observe the growth of the plants every day. Measure the height of the grass and record it on the graph paper."

Measure each plant and then find an average...

"Use a yellow marker to show the height of the seeds grown in the light and black for those grown in the dark."

After several days of visible growth ...

"Is this what you expected to happen?"

"Are you surprised? Why do you think the grass in the dark is growing so well?"

"What are the two parts of the seed? ... What can you tell me about the embryo and the cotyledon?"

After several more days ...

"How is the grass grown in the dark different from the grass grown in the light?"
(Answer: Check the answer key.)

"Why do you think some of the grass is yellow and some green?"

"Which plants do you think are going to survive? ... Why do you think so?"
(Answer: Check the answer key.)

"How could you test to see if the darkness makes the grass turn yellow?"

"Take one of the planters that has yellow grass and set it in the indirect light. Put one of the planters with green grass that was grown in the light and set it in the dark."

"What do you think is going to happen? ... Why do you think so? Carefully keep track of what happens."

After a week or so...

"What happened to the grass when it was moved from the dark to the light? ... From the light to the dark?"

The idea -

"In the experiment you were investigating light and dark on the growth of plants."

"Where all the other factors the same?"

"Describe what happened to the four planters."

"What do you think now about what light does for plants?"

"Yes, light is important for plants. But how can you explain why the plants grew in the dark for a while?"

"Think back on the last activity. What are the parts to a seed? Is it possible that one of the parts to a seed would provide the necessary food to grow?"

"When a plant first starts to grow, it gets its food from the cotyledon. Now you know the purpose of this part of the seed."

"Plants need food for growth, just as people and animals do. Where does their food come from?"

"Is water and soil all that a plant needs to live?"

"Plants grown in the dark died. When you moved those that had turned yellow into the light, they turned green and grew. Wasn't the soil the same in every cup? How can you explain what happened?"

"What made the difference?"
(Answer: Check the answer key.)

"When sunlight reaches a plant, the plant takes in some of the sun's energy. The plant uses that energy with air, water, and chemicals for making food. There is a special word for this food-making process:

Photosynthesis."

"Do you think that the grass grown in the dark would have stayed green if you would have fertilized the soil?"

"Repeat this experiment but to the grass grown in the dark you will add fertilizer."

At the end of this experiment ...

"Did the fertilizer make any difference?"
(Answer: No, the grass grown in the dark still turned yellow and died.)

"What does this lead you to believe about the importance of the sun for plants?"

ACTIVITY 30:
OBSERVING GOD'S CREATION

MATERIALS
ziplock bags
magnifier

OVERVIEW: EXPLORING THE CONCEPT - COMMUNITIES

LESSON PLAN

MATERIALS OR INFORMATION I NEED	WHAT I AM TO DO AND TO CONSIDER
1. This activity is best suited for a day of exploration at an undeveloped environmental area. Nature trails with ponds or lakes are wonderful. Many state or national parks are excellent. An alternate or supplemental activity would be to use colorful books from the library that show different habitats or communities of animals and plants.	"Plants and animals are an important part of God's creation. Wherever you go, you are likely to see them. The kinds you see may be different. You might see the unique foliage of the rain forest of Washington or the gnarled cypresses in Louisiana. You might see a beautiful red pheasant in South Dakota or an armadillo in texas." "Plants and animals when grouped together are called **Organisms.**"
2. Let the following questions be a guide to you and your family as you explore God's creation firsthand. Take along ziplock bags to collect specimens. These are just some suggestions of questions. Be creative and enjoy the beauty of God's creation! Note: You will need a small dead animal and a dead plant. (Such as a cricket and leaf) to be used in activity 32. When you return home proceed to the next activity before finishing this one.	"Make a list of every kind of organism you see. Also try to estimate how many of each you see. If you don't know the name, make a sketch of it."

"Use these plastic bags to collect some of the plants and animals."

"Look in as many different places as you can think of to find the organisms. Did you look under some of these rocks? ... What is this growing on the bark of this fallen tree? ... What is this floating of the pond? ... Let's take home a sample of water to see if there are any animals you can observe with a microscope."

If your children find fungi or some other 'strange' type of organism that they are not familiar, then they should sketch its shape, describe its color, habitat, etc. Further research can be done later at the library .

"Which organisms are animals? ... Plants? Are there some you are not sure of?"

"A group of the same kind of organism in an area is called a

Population."

Let's see how many different populations can you find?"

"Look at the diagram below:

Seeds —> mouse —> owl

"This diagram represents the feeding relationship. It means that seeds are eaten by a mouse which in turn is eaten by an owl. Such a diagram is called a

Food chain."

"Find organisms that make a food chain. Draw the food chain for several groups of organisms in this area."

"How is a food chain like the energy chain?"

3. In the next sample conversation I assume that you observed seeds, crickets, frogs, birds, and cats. You may have to modify the dialog to match what you observed.

"Did you see more seeds than crickets? ... More crickets than frogs?"

"Did you see more seeds than birds? ... More birds than cats?"

"Which population is the largest?
(Answer: Check the answer key.)

Which population is the smallest?"
(Answer: Check the answer key.)

"Do all the living things in the area have enough food to eat?"

"What would happen if they did not?"
(Answer: Check the answer key.)

Seed—> cricket —> frog

"What does this diagram mean?"

"Let's suppose that 10 frogs eat 90 crickets each day."

"How many crickets on the average would one frog eat per day?"
(Answer: Check the answer key.)

"If one cricket eat 15 seeds per day, how many seeds would be needed to support a frog for one day?"
(Answer: Check the answer key.)

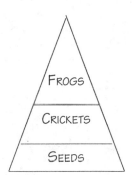

"Look at the diagram of these relationships."

"For a frog to survive one week how many seeds would need to be in the area?"
(Answer: Check the answer key.)

"This diagram is referred to as a

Food pyramid."

"What would happen if all the seeds were destroyed?"

"What would this do the animals in this area?"

4. Using the combined list of all the different organisms you observed…

"Circle all the **plants**. Include grass, seeds, weeds, flowers, trees, etc."

"The remaining list contains animals."

"Next, draw a box around all those animals that eat only plants."

"These animals are called plant-eaters?"

"Now, look at the last group. What can you tell me about these animals? … What do they eat?"

5. Look at the chart below as you think about your observations. The major section is divided into three sections. The sections on the right side and bottom will be used in a later activity.

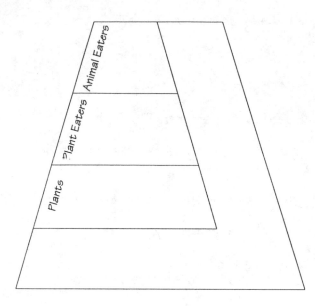

"You will use this chart to help organize your observations. Organizing information in a certain way often makes it easy to see patterns and relationships."

"In the third section from the top write the names of all the plants on your list. Also write down the estimated number of each plant."

"In the second section write the names of everything on your list that eats plants."

"In the top section write the names of everything that eats the organisms listed in the second and third sections"

"Draw arrows on the chart to show what is being eaten."

ACTIVITY 31
COMMUNITY INTERACTIONS

MATERIALS
baby food jars, 6
dead plants and animals from Activity 100 (crickets and leaves work well)
magnifier, microscope (optional)
sand

OVERVIEW: EXPLORING THE CONCEPT - COMMUNITIES

LESSON PLAN

MATERIALS OR INFORMATION I NEED	WHAT I AM TO DO AND TO CONSIDER
1. You will need the materials listed above.	"Examine the dead organisms you collected."
	"Observe each organism beneath the magnifier."
	"What would have happened to these if you had left them where they were?"
	"What happens to a dead organism when it is buried?"
	"Put enough sand to cover the bottom of the six jars."
	"Then put one dead animal in jar #1 and #2. Place it next to the sides so you can watch what happens."
	"Place a dead plant part next to the sides of jars #3 and #4."
	"Add sand to all six jars so that they are two-thirds full. Put only sand in jars #5 and #6 ""
	"Fill jars one, three, and five with water."
	"Jars two, four, and six will not have water added."
	"Label the contents of each jar with what is inside it. For example jar #1 should read 'sand-water-animal'."
	"Also record the date."
2. Do not open the jars for about 2 weeks.	"Observe what happens inside the jars over the next two weeks. Keep a record of what you observe. Do not take off the lids."

"Why do you think the experiment was designed the way it was?"

"Why did you put water in three and no water in three?"
(Answer: Check the answer key.)

During the two week observational period ...

"Carefully observe the jars. What do you see? Use the magnifier to observe what is happening?

How do the jars compare?"

"How are they different?"

"What changes are there?"

"What is happening to the organisms?"

"What do you think will happen if you continue to watch the jars for several more weeks?"

The idea -

"The fuzzy, dark greenish objects that you see in the jars are tiny plants. Each plant is a

Mold.

A mold is a very small living plant, a microorganism. It can grow and develop in the jars."

"What do you think molds use for food?"

"What evidence do you have to support your idea?"

"From your experiment what can you tell about the type of environment needed for molds to grow?"

3. An expansion of this activity would be to show mold growing on bread. Another activity showing the effect of mold would be to set a moistened orange peel in a ziplock bag.

"Use the magnifier to carefully observe what is on the bread/orange peel?". What do you think it is? ... Why do you think so?"

4. After several more weeks open the jars. Conduct this activity outside!

Caution! Some people are sensitive to various kinds of mold, especially if they happen to breathe some of the mold into their lungs. Wash your hands after handling moldy objects.

The idea -

The organisms should be decayed so that you may not see them.

5. You will need a banana, orange, grape, and six baby food jars.

"Take the baby food jars outside and carefully open the lids."

"What do you observe that you were not able to observe before?"
(Answer: A terrible smell.)

"The bad odor is not caused by mold, but by another organism."

"This organism is a

Bacterium.

The plural of bacterium is

Bacteria.

These tiny organisms are found almost everywhere. Some are beneficial while others are harmful."

"Carefully pour the materials onto a paper towel. Use the popsicle stick to spread out the contents."

"Use your magnifier to observe the plants and animals that you buried."

"What do you observe?"

"What has happened to the dead plants and animals?"

"The dead organisms have been taken apart by the mold and bacteria."

"This process is called

Decomposition.

"Decompose means to take apart."

"Mold and bacteria are very important decomposers. They break apart the dead organisms."

"Cut two slices of each fruit."

"Set one slice into each jar."

Get some yeast.

"Sprinkle yeast over one banana, orange and grape slice."

"Close the jars with lids."

"Label the contents of the jars."

"The purpose of the three jars with no yeast is for comparison."

"Take a whole banana and remove two strips of skin. Sprinkle yeast on half of the exposed banana. Set the banana in a quart jar and tightly seal."

"Each day describe the fruit with yeast and the fruit without yeast."

"How have the pieces of fruit changed?"

"What differences are there between the pieces of fruit with yeast and those without yeast?"

"What do you think caused the fruit to change?"

"Now you have seen yeast interact with pieces of fruit."

"Yeast is a tiny plant."

"Like mold and bacteria, yeast is a

Decomposer.

Ask your mom about the importance of yeast in the bread making process.

---

6. You will need 2 planters, soil, and grass seeds.

"What purpose do decomposers have in nature?"

"Do an experiment to see if you can gain some understanding of the purpose of these tiny little decomposers."

"Plant grass seeds in these cups."

"Make sure they are exactly the same - the same amount and kind of soil, the same amount of light."

"Now, water one planter with plain tap water."

"Water the other cup with water mixed with the materials left from the yeast banana experiment."

"Make sure they receive the same amount of liquid."

"What variable are you investigating?"
(Answer: Check the answer key.)

"Carefully watch the growth of the grass in the two cups."

"What differences have you observed?"

"How have the grass seeds used the materials which are left from decomposition?."

"What does this experiment lead you to believe about the purpose of decomposers?"

The idea -

Look again at the chart on page 112..

"You have finished your experiments with mold, bacteria, and yeast. These three tiny organisms need to be added to your chart."

"Where do you think they should be added?"

"Since they are plants, you might think they should be added to that section. However, mold, bacteria, and yeast are different from ordinary green plants. They cannot make food for themselves."

"You will use the section on the right side of the chart. Write the three names there."

"What is it that these organisms do?"
(Answer: Check the answer key.)

"That's right. They break apart dead organisms. Label this section '**decomposers**.'"

"Now, draw some arrows on the chart showing the sources of food for the decomposers."

"As you have seen, some matter is left when decomposers are through with a food source. Plants make use of the materials which are left."

"The materials which are left are minerals, gases, and water. Anything that is left over after food is broken down by yeast, molds, or bacteria, is called

Raw materials.

"Write '**raw materials**' at the bottom of the chart."

"Use a marker to draw an arrow from molds, yeast, and bacteria to raw materials."

"Because the plants use the raw materials, use the marker to draw an arrow from raw materials up to plants."

"Do you remember how plants make food?"

"The process is called **photosynthesis**. The sun interacts with the plants enabling them to produce their own food."

"Because the sun is so important, draw it in the upper left side of the chart. Then use the marker to draw an arrow from it to the plants."

"Study the chart to see some of the interactions or shifts of food sources."

"Look at the arrows on the chart."

"Do you see a general pattern?"

"What kind of pattern do the arrows make?"

"Starting with the raw materials the arrows move through plants, to plant-eaters, to animal-eaters, to molds-bacteria-yeast, and back to raw materials."

"This pattern is called the

Food cycle."

"What do the arrows represent?"

"Yes, they show food or energy transfer."

Look at the plant section ...

"Plants make food for all organisms. Because they make, or produce, food for themselves and for all organisms, they are called

Producers.

"Write the word '**producers**' across the bottom section."

Point to the plant-eater and animal-eater section ...

"What do these animals do?"

"Because they eat, or consume, the food produced by plants, they are called

Consumers.

"Write the word '**consumers**' across the middle and upper section."

"What are raw materials?"

"What is the relationship between decomposers and producers?"

"What is the relationship between producers and consumers?"

"What is the relationship between consumers and decomposers?"

"What role does the sun play in the food cycle?"

"Plants and animals within a certain area are shown on your chart. The chart summarizes the interactions among the living things. The **food cycle** is an example of interaction and of the relationship among the plants and animals."

"Organisms in an area interacting in this kind of relationship can be called a

Community."

"Each part of a community is dependent upon other parts. There are interactions between one living thing and other living things. There are also interactions between living things and nonliving parts of the environment. One population is dependent upon another population. This dependency holds the community together."

"Write '**community**' across the top of the chart."

---

7. Use the world book encyclopedia or some other similar source.

"Look up **pond** in the world book."

"Use the information from the world book to complete the chart labeled 'pond community.'"

---

8. Repeat step 7 for desert community, forest community, and prairie community.

"Compare these four charts with the one that describes the organisms you observed."
"How are they alike? ... Different?"

"Which of these charts is most like your chart?"

"What does that lead you to believe about the kind of area you observed? ... Is it more like the desert? ...Pond? ...Prairie? ... Or forest?"

"How does man fit into this community picture?"

"Some people say that man is simply an animal. That he has evolved from lower forms of animals. This is the secular view of man. He is simply a more complex animal."

"Others say that man is a special creation of God. In this view he is more than an animal. Though man may have some similar body characteristics to animals, his ability to reason, create, and worship indicate that man is unique."

"Read Genesis 1 and 2."

"Man was set into a perfect community. Describe the original relationship of Adam and Eve to their community as described in Genesis 1 and 2."

ACTIVITY 32
COMMUNITY INTERACTIONS
— A Continuation —

MATERIALS
Community Picture
Community Chart

OVERVIEW: EXPLORING THE CONCEPT - ECOSYSTEM

LESSON PLAN

MATERIALS OR INFORMATION I NEED	WHAT I AM TO DO AND TO CONSIDER
1. Study the Community Picture and Community Chart.	"Look at the community picture and chart. Name some of the plants and animals in the picture. Also, find them on the chart."
	"The chart has four sections. Most of the names are listed in the three of the sections."
	"The lowest section contains the names of plants."
	"The middle section lists those that eat plants."
	"The top section lists those that feed on plant-eaters."
	"The arrows on the chart show the direction of the food supply. For instance, as the arrows indicate, a population of plants is eaten by one of insects. The insects, in turn, are eaten by a population of birds. A population of birds is eaten by cats."
	"Parts of dying plants and animals are in the picture. Dead plants and animals decay and decompose. Their remains return to the soil. The chart provides a place to represent this information."
	"Mold, bacteria, and yeast are listed at the side of the chart. These tiny living things feed on the dead organisms. When the decomposers interact to take what they need, gases and water are left. These substances are called raw materials. The chart shows the raw materials being returned to the soil." "Notice the arrow going upward from the raw materials to the plant section. This represents the plants' use of the materials. The plants use the raw materials to make food."

"Plants are the only organisms which can make food. Because this is true, they are often called the producers of food energy. To make food, green plants must have light. Write the word 'light' beside the plant section of the chart."

"Notice how the arrows on the chart flow around as in a circle. This forms a model of a food cycle. The model enables us to see how the flow of food moves in a circular direction. It is not possible to see all the interactions just by looking at the picture. So, in this case, a chart model gives more useful information."

"The populations of organisms within an area interact with one another. They interact in the ways which are shown in the picture and in the chart. Because of this interaction, the populations can be called a **biotic community**. The word 'biotic' refers to life and living things. Each living thing is dependent on another, and together they are called a **community**.

"What do the plants depend upon?"
(Answer: Check the answer key.)

"What is in the middle section of the chart? And what do they depend upon for food?"
(Answer: Check the answer key.)

"What about the top section?"
(Answer: Check the answer key.)

"What do the arrows show?"
(Answer: Check the answer key.)

"What role do the decomposers play in a community?"
(Answer: Check the answer key.)

"We started with raw materials and have now ended with raw materials. This describes the food cycle. To complete the chart you need to see how the living community interacts with the environment."

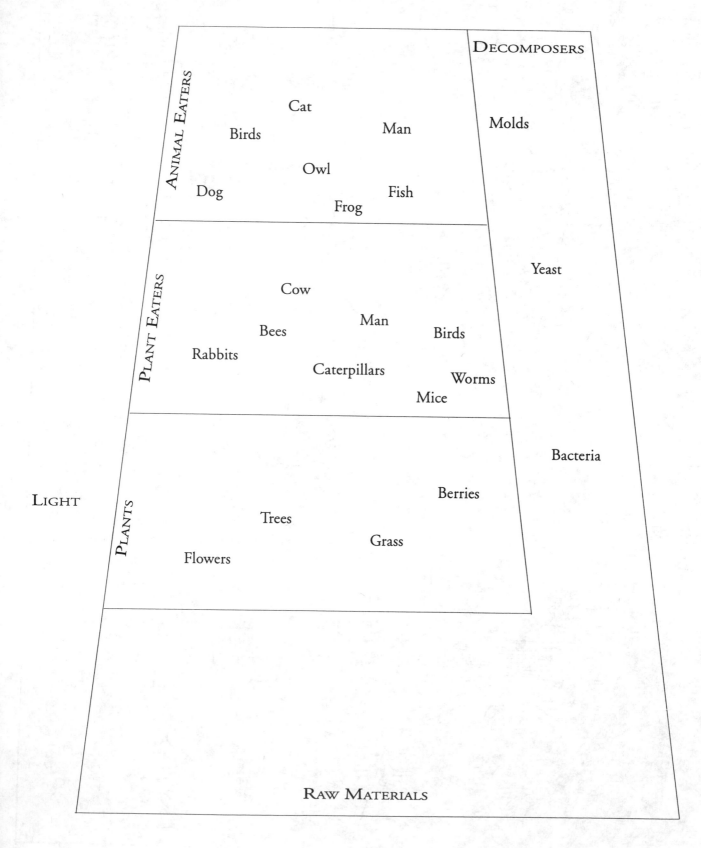

DECOMPOSERS

Molds

Yeast

Bacteria

ANIMAL EATERS

Cat

Birds

Man

Owl

Dog

Fish

Frog

PLANT EATERS

Cow

Bees

Man

Birds

Rabbits

Caterpillars

Worms

Mice

LIGHT

PLANTS

Berries

Trees

Grass

Flowers

RAW MATERIALS

ACTIVITY 33
"THE POWER OF GOD"
— Begin this activity after completing Activity 22 Slopes —

MATERIALS
Bible

OVERVIEW: EXPANDING THE CONCEPT - ENERGY

MATERIALS OR INFORMATION I NEED	WHAT I AM TO DO AND TO CONSIDER
1. You will need the observation sheet and the list of Bible verses.	"Look up each Bible verse."
	"As you read the verses think about a who question, a what question, when, where, why, and how questions."
	"What does this verse mean?"
Look up only a few verses at a time.	"What words or ideas are repeated in these verses?"
	"What is the relationship between the believer, the Holy Spirit, and the power of God?"
	"What are some of the things the Holy Spirit does according to these few verses?"
	"Who is the source of power to live the Christian life?"
	"Are Christians the energy source or the energy receiver?"
	"Draw a picture of the energy transfer?"
	"The Greek word for power in these verses is 'dunamis'. This is the root word for the English word dynamite."

OBSERVATION SHEET

As you are observing the verses, ask ...

WHO?   WHAT?   WHEN?   WHERE?   WHY ?   HOW?

• WORDS AND IDEAS THAT ARE REPEATED

• CONNECTIVES: SUCH AS, BUT, AND, IF, SINCE, THEN, THEREFORE

• CONTRASTS (DIFFERENCES)

• QUESTIONS & ANSWERS

• COMMANDS & PROMISES

• ATTITUDES TOWARD: GOD   CHRIST   OTHERS

USE THE OBSERVATION SHEET TO HELP YOU OBSERVE THESE VERSES.

VERSE	WHAT DOES IT SAY?	WHAT DOES IT MEAN?
Acts 1:8	WHO: the disciples; WHAT: will receive power; WHEN: the Holy Spirit; WHAT: witnesses	The disciples' life would be different after the Holy Spirit was given. They would have power to witness.
Acts 3:12		
Acts 4:7		
Acts 4:33		
Acts 6:8		
Acts 10:38		
Romans 1:4		
Romans 1:16		
Romans 1:20		
Romans 15:13		
Romans 15:18, 19		

I Corinthians 1:18

I Corinthians 1:22-24

I Corinthians 2:4, 5

I Corinthians 4:20

I Corinthians 6:14

II Corinthians 4:7

II Corinthians 6:7

II Corinthians 12:9

II Corinthians 13:4

Ephesians 1:19

Ephesians 3:7

Ephesians 3:20

Philippians 3:10

I Thessalonians 1:5

II Thessalonians 1:11

II Timothy 1:7,8

Hebrews 1: 3

I Peter 1: 5

II Peter 1:3

ACTIVITY 34
CHRIST LIVING IN ME

MATERIALS
Bible

OVERVIEW: EXPANDING THE CONCEPT - ENERGY

MATERIALS OR INFORMATION I NEED	WHAT I AM TO DO AND TO CONSIDER

"In the introduction to the Phillip's translation of the New Testament Letters, he states:

The great difference between present-day Christianity and that of which we read in these letters, is that to us, it is primarily a performance; to them, it was a real experience. We are apt to reduce the Christian religion to a code or at best, a rule of heart and life. To these men it is quite plainly the invasion of their lives by a new quality of life altogether. They do not hesitate to describe this as Christ living in them.

1. Read I Corinthians 2:11
What does this verse tell us about the Holy Spirit?

2. Read Ephesians 4:30
What does this verse tell us about the Holy Spirit?

3. Read Acts 5:3,4
"In verse 3, to whom does it say Ananias lied?

In verse 4, to whom does it say Ananias lied?

What does this say about the Holy Spirit?

4. Read Hebrews 9:14
What characteristic is used to describe the Holy Spirit?

5. Read John 16:13-14
What do these verses tell us about the Holy Spirit?

6. Read John 3:5,6
How does a person become a Christian and receive spiritual life?

7. Read John 7:37-39
How did Jesus describe the life the Holy Spirit would produce in the Christian?

8. Read Galatians 5:22,23 and I Corinthians 13
What do these verses tell us?

These are the characteristics of God himself. These are characteristics which the Holy Spirit will produce in the life of the spirit controlled Christian.

Most Christians, however, do not demonstrate these qualities consistently in their lives. The most important question then is: How can I allow God to produce these qualities in me?

9. Read Romans 7: 14-24
What word is repeated over and over?

How many times is the word 'i' used is these verses?

What is Paul saying about himself?

10. Read Romans 6:1-19
Paul raises two significant questions in these verses. Look at verse 1 and verse 15.

According to verses 1-14, what is the basis for your no longer choosing to sin?

What do these verses say about what happened to Jesus?

What do these verses say is true about us as Christians?

We believe that Jesus died for our sins, and that is true, but what does this say about us?

In verses 15-19, Paul seems to say that we have to make a choice. Describe that choice.

11. Read the selection from MY UTMOST FOR HIS HIGHEST.

12. Read Romans 7:24-8:17
Paul contrasts two words, to ideas. What two words are repeated in these verses?
What is Paul saying about living the Christian life?

How does a person live under the control of the Holy Spirit and not under the influence of the flesh?

13. Read Ephesians 2:8
How does a person become a Christian?

14. Read Colossians 2:6
If you received Christ by faith, how do you live the Christian life?

15. Read Ephesians 5:18
What command is given to us in this verse?

Would God ever command us to do something he doesn't want us to do?

Is it God's will that each of us be filled with the Holy Spirit?

If we ask him to fill us, assuming we want him to and assuming we have confessed any known sin, will he fill us with the Holy Spirit? How do you know?

16. Read I John 5:14, 15
What does John say about asking any thing in agreement with God?

17. Read romans 6:11 and Ephesians 5:18
According to these two verses, what are we to do?

Is it God's will that we consider ourselves dead to sin and alive to God? ... Is it God's will that we be controlled by his Holy Spirit?

18. Read the selection from ABSOLUTE SURRENDER by Andrew Murray.

19. Read the selection from TWO CONTENTS TWO REALITIES by Dr. Schaeffer.

"I HAVE BEEN CRUCIFIED WITH CHRIST." GAL.2:20

The imperative need spiritually is to sign the death warrant of the disposition of sin, to turn all emotional impressions and intellectual beliefs into a moral verdict against the disposition of sin - my claim to my right to myself. Paul says - "I have been crucified with Christ'" he does not say -"I will endeavor to follow Him: - but - "I have been identified with Him in His death." When I come to such a moral decision and act upon it, then all that Christ wrought for me on the Cross is wrought in me. The free committal of myself to God gives the Holy Spirit the chance to impart to me the holiness of Jesus Christ.

"...nevertheless I live ..." The individuality remains, but the mainspring, the ruling disposition, is radically altered. The same human body remains, but the old satanic right to myself is destroyed.

"And the life which I now live in the flesh ...," not the life which I long to live and pray to live, but the life I now live in my mortal flesh, the life which men can see, "I live by the faith of the Son of God." This faith is not Paul's faith in Jesus Christ, but the faith that the Son of God has imparted to him - "the faith of the Son of God." It is no longer faith in faith but faith which has overleapt all conscious bounds, the identical faith of the Son of God.

Absolute Surrender
by Andrew Murray

I wish to try and put before you what the blessedness is of a life filled with the Holy Spirit. It may please God to make our desire so strong, and to make us see so clearly. This is just what I need. I cannot live longer without it, that He may bring us to receive more than we ever expected. He is a God who is willing and able to do above what we can ask or think.

I do not think I can put the blessedness of being filled with the Spirit more clearly before you than by just pointing to the wonderful change which Pentecost made in the lives of the disciples. I think that is one of the most wonderful object-lessons in the whole of Scripture - those twelve men under Christ's training for three years, and yet remaining, apparently, at such a distance from the life they ought to live; and then all at once, but the blessed incoming of the Holy Spirit, being made just what God wanted them to be.

Look first at the change that Pentecost wrought in their relationship to Jesus. During His life on earth with them they could not have Him within them. There He was outside, separated from them - very near, very loving; and yet, if I may say so with deep reverence, what a failure Christ's teaching of them was until the Holy Spirit came! Christ taught them humility, time after time. He said, "Learn of Me, for I am meek and lowly in heart" He said, time after time, "He that humbleth himself shall be exalted." Yet at the Holy Communion table there they were, still contending which of them should be chief. Christ did not conquer their pride. This was not for the want of divine teaching. Why was it, then? It was because on one thing: Christ was still outside of them, and He could not get into their heart to dwell there. It was impossible; the time had not come, and there they had the divine, almighty, blessed Redeemer along with them, but still outside. And how different they were from Him! To teach us that no outward instruction, even from Christ Himself, or His words in Holy Scripture, can bring us the true and full blessing, till the Holy Spirit works it in us.

But what a change took place on the day of Pentecost! "At that day ye shall know that I am in you." What does that mean? Christ in us, just the same as we are in this building?" No, we are in the building, but we can go out of it again, and we do not suffer anything by it. I live in a house, but I can leave that house and go elsewhere. The building and the house and I are not vitally, organically connected. [This relationship is more like what happens when we step into an airplane. As long as we remain in the plane we have all the characteristics of the plane — we can fly! However, the moment we step out of it we fall to the ground.] But the Lord Jesus came to be - I say it with reverence - part of those disciples, to fill their heart and thought and affection; and what Peter and James and John had, when they had Christ alongside of them, you and I have in a much larger measure, if we have the living Christ within us.

And how did that change come? By the Holy Spirit. "At that day" - when the Spirit comes - "ye shall know that I am in you'" for the Father will love you, and I will love you, and we will come and make our home in you.

Oh! Does not your heart long for it? I have thought and thought and thought of Jesus in Bethlehem, and of Jesus on Calvary, and of Jesus upon the throne, and I have worshipped and loved and rejoiced exceedingly in Him; but all the time I wanted something better and something deeper and something nearer. Will you not give up yourselves for this blessing - to be filled with the Spirit, that the blessed Jesus may be able to take possession of you? Is not that what your heart longs for? Jesus within - the very Jesus, who is the Almighty One, who died on the Cross and sits upon the throne, condescending to be our life?

And that is what the Spirit comes for. Jesus said, "He will glorify Me, for He will take of Mine and show it unto you." And what is the glory of Jesus? His love and His power. And the Holy Spirit will reveal Christ in us, so that the wonderful love of Christ shall be a possession and a reality in its divine nearness, and that power of Christ shall have the mastery within us. You know that wonderful prayer in Ephesians 3, that the Father might strengthen them with might by the Spirit in the inner man, that Christ might dwell in their heart. The mighty power of the Holy spirit can do it. The Holy Spirit makes Jesus present with us.

And then, the second thought in connection with the change wrought in the disciples: not only was Jesus outside of them, but Jesus was not always with them. They could not every moment be with Him ... There came times of separation, and at last there came that terrible death, that awful separation from them in this world. Yes, Christ was their life - sometimes with Christ, and sometimes not with Him; sometimes near Him, and sometimes the crowd pressing around Him, and they could not get to Him.

But, ah! friends, the presence of Jesus by the Holy Spirit is meant to be unbroken, continual, and for ever. Is not that what your heart longs for? Do not you know what it is sometimes to live a week or a month in a joy that makes your heart sing all the day. And the change comes, and the cloud and the darkness come - and you do not know why it is - sometimes with bodily sickness or depression, sometimes with the cares and the difficulties of this life, sometimes with the conscious-ness of your own failure. Oh, child of God, would that I could tell it you and see it myself! Jesus does love you; He does not wish to be separated from you one minute; He cannot bear it. We want to believe in that love of Jesus. No mother ever so delighted in the baby she has in her arms as does the Christ of God in you. He wants to be most intimate with you, and to have most unceasing fellowship with you.

Another thought. Look at the change it made in their own inner life. It was, up to Pentecost, a life of failure and of weakness. I have spoken of their pride. Christ had to reprove them for their pride, time after time...

But what a change when Pentecost came! When the Holy Spirit - the Spirit of God - became their life, they were filled with the might and the power of the living Jesus, the Saviour from sin. There is that accursed self that will have its say in everything, and there is no power that can expel that but the power of the presence of Jesus.

You may get troubled about some theological definition, as to how it is all done, as to how much sin there remains, and how much there is cast out, but what we want you to believe is this: that though you cannot explain and expound all, believe that the Spirit of holiness which will be given is the holiness of Jesus in your heart, and be content with that. Filled with the Spirit, you have within you the power of the holiness of God to do the blessed work of sanctification.

And then, the third thought in regard to this wonderful blessedness of being filled with the Spirit. Look at the love that united them into one body ...

Do you want to have a heat overflowing with love to every child of God, to all the children of God outside your own circle? Do you want a heart of love that can set others on fire? Do you want the very love of heaven to flow out from you? Do you want the self-sacrificing love of Jesus to take possession of you, so that you can bear and forbear, so that with the long-suffering and tenderness and gentleness, and the very meekness of Christ, the Lamb of God, you are willing to be the helper and servant of everyone, however unlovable or unlovely? Then you need to be filled with the Spirit ...

Just let me give you four very little words as steps. Let now everyone who longs for this blessing say, first of all I must be filled. Say it to God in the depth of your heart. God commands it; I cannot live my life as I should live without it.

Then, say as the second step: I may be filled. It is possible the promise is for me. Settle that, and let all doubt vanish. These apostles, once so full of pride and of self-life, were filled with the Holy Spirit because they clave unto Jesus. And, with all you sinfulness, if you will but cling to Him you may be filled.

Then, thirdly, say: I would be filled. To get the 'pearl of great price' you must sell all, you must give up everything. You are willing, are you not? Everything, Lord, if I may only have that. Lord, I would have it from Thee to-night.

And then comes the last step: I shall be filled. God longs to give it; I shall have it. Never mind whether it come tonight as a flood, or in deep silence... Oh, claim it tonight; I shall. My God, it is so solemn, it is almost awful; it is too blessed and too true - Lord, wilt Thou not do it? My trembling heart says, I shall be filled with the Holy Spirit. Oh, say to God, "Father, I shall, for the name of my Saviour is Jesus, who saves from all sin, and who fills with the Holy Spirit."

TWO CONTENTS, TWO REALITIES
by Dr. Francis Schaeffer

There are four things which I think are absolutely necessary if we as Christians are going to meet the need of our age and the overwhelming pressure we are increasingly facing. They are two contents and two realities:

The First Content: Sound Doctrine

The Second Content: Honest Answers to Honest Questions

The First Reality: True Spirituality

The Second Reality: The Beauty of Human Relationships

… Back in 1951 and 1952, I went through a very deep time in may own life. I had been a pastor for ten years and a missionary for another five, and I was connected with a group who stood very strongly for the truth of the Scriptures. But as I watched, it became clear to me that I saw very little spiritual reality. I had to ask why. I looked at myself as well and realized that my own spiritual reality was not as great as it had been immediately after my conversion. We were in Switzerland at that time, and I said to my wife, "I must really think this through.:"

I took about two months, and I walked in the mountains whenever it was clear. And when it was rainy, I walked back and forth in the hayloft over our chalet. I thought and wrestled and prayed, and I went all the way back to my agnosticism. I asked myself whether I had been right to stop being an agnostic and to become a Christian. I told my wife, if it didn't turn out right I was going to be honest and go back to America and put it all aside and do some other work.

I came to realize that indeed I had been right in becoming a Christian. But then I went on further and wrestled deeper and asked, "But then where is the spiritual reality, Lord, among most of that which calls itself orthodoxy?" And gradually I found something. I found something that I had not been taught, a simple thing but profound. I discovered the meaning of the work of Christ, the meaning of the blood of Christ, moment by moment in our lives after we are Christians — the moment-by-moment work of the whole Trinity in our lives because as Christians we are indwelt by the Holy Spirit. That is true spirituality.

For a complete explanation by Dr. Schaeffer we encourage you to read his book, True Spirituality. This book is available from THE CORNERSTONE CURRICULUM PROJECT.

Page 1
Mystery Powder:
Tablespoon of each of the following:
        baking powder
        salt
        oatmeal
Put one tablespoon of the salt, baking powder, and oatmeal in the small jar. Stir the powders thoroughly.

Page 3
"WHAT WOULD BE A GOOD NAME FOR THIS SYSTEM?"
(Answer: The fruit basket system or something similar.)

Page 4
"What did you say was in it? Name the parts to this system."
(Answer: Salt, baking soda, oatmeal, jar.)

"What are the subsystems in your 'powder system'?"
(Answer: Oatmeal, salt, baking powder, and jar.)

Page 10
Compare these crystals with some salt crystals.
What do you think is in the lid? What evidence do you have that this is salt?"
(Answer: Salt. The shape of the crystals.)

Page 13
"What difference does temperature make on the amount of sugar dissolved?"
(Answer: The higher the temperature, the greater the amount of sugar dissolved.)

Page 15
"The parts of a system are called the subsystems. Name the subsystems of your interacting swinging system."
(Answer: Seat, chain, top bar, legs, and me.)

Page 17
"In this experiment what was the variable....what did you change?"
(Answer: How high I was released.)

"Make a statement about the distance you are pulled back and the number of cycles you go in one minute."
(Answer: The number of cycles does not change by changing the release point.)

"What part of the system have you changed? What variable are you investigating?"
(Answer: The weight.)

Page 19
"What were the three variables that you tested?"
(Answer: Height released, weight, and length.)

"Describe how changing each variable changes the number of cycles in one minute?"
(Answer: Changing the height and weight made little or no difference; changing the length of the chain made the cycle change.)

Page 22
"What were the variables you investigated?"
(Answer: How high the ball was dropped from the floor, and the type of ball.)

Page 23
"What variables did you investigate?"
(Answer: Different balls and different floors.)

"To make a fair comparison of the how much a ball bounces what must you do?"
(Answer: Keep all the variables but one the same.)

"What are some of the variables you would need to control in a race?"
(Answer: Starting time, distance, etc.)

Page 25
"Name the variables you are investigating?"
(Answer: Size of the ball and color.)

"Which variables must you control?"
(Answer: The distance that the ball falls, the surface that it drops onto.)

Page 27
"What variables did you investigate?"
(Answer: Release point, weight, and length of the string.)

Page 28
Which variable or variables affect the swing of the pendulum system?
(Answer: The length of the string.)

"What would have happened if the length of the string were not controlled?"

Which variables did not seem to affect the swing of the pendulum?"
(Answer: The release point, and the weight.)

"Does this system remind you of another system you investigated?
(Answer: The swing system.)

Page 34
"Suppose you look out your bedroom window and see the tree limbs of a large tree moving. What could be several possible causes for this event?"
(Answer: The wind, someone pushing on the limbs, someone climbing in the tree.)

"What if someone told you that your brother or sister were blowing against the large tree. Would that be an adequate cause for this event?
(Answer: No.)

Page 32
"Look at the graphs. Do you see any major changes in the quantitative data? ... How would you describe these changes?"
(Answer: The air and ground temperature went down; the amount of precipitation went down.)

"What do you think could have caused these two plants to grow differently?"
(Answer: Temperature, moisture, light, fertilizer, disease, etc.)

Page 33
"Are there variables or factors that might affect the growth of plants that you should control?"
(Answer: Yes: Amount of light, amount of heat, amount of fertilizer, etc.)

Page 34
"What variable or factor are you investigating?"
(Answer: Moisture.)

"What variables are you going to control?"
(Answer: The amount of light, fertilizer, & heat.)

Page 39
"What factor are you investigating in this experiment?"
(Answer: The number of seeds per cup.)

Page 44
"What is the one variable you are investigating?
(Answer: Amount of plant food.)

"What was the range of the plant food you tested?"
(Answer: 0 to 2 tablespoonfuls per quart of water)

"Can you see an optimum range?"
(Answers will vary.)

Page 47
"What chemicals are in the bottle."
(Answer: Nitrogen, phosphoric acid, and potash.)

"Now what do you think the three numbers on the front side of the label represent?"
(Answer: The percentage of these three chemicals.)

"What factor or variable are you investigating?"
(Answer: A specific chemical.)

Page 49
What variable are you testing?
(Answer: Soil type.)

Page 51
"What are some factors that you have tested?"
(Answer: Amount of moisture, closeness of seeds, amount and type of chemicals, and soil types are variables that you have tested.)

"What are some variables that you have not tested?"
(Answers will vary - light, temperature.)

Page 54
"Why is it be important to test for one variable at a time?"
(Answer: To identify the proper cause and effect relationship.)

Page 55
"If you wanted to test just for moisture, how would you set up the experiment?"
(Answer: The box would contain both wet & dry with no light.)

Page 64
"How could you test the property of the length of the rubber band?"
(Answer: Using a long rubber band and a short rubber band.)

"How could you test the property of width of the rubber band?"
(Answer: Use wide and narrow rubber bands.)

"Design an experiment to test each property. When you test a property for its effect on shooting distances, what has the property become?"
(Answer: A variable.)

Page 65
"This temperature is important. The ice melted at this temperature. What would be a good name for this temperature?"
(Answer: The melting point of ice.)

Page 76
"Draw a diagram that represents the energy chain as you ride your bike."
(Answer: Rider —> pedals —> chain —> rear wheel)

"What evidence of energy transfer do you have?"
(Answer: The bike moves.)

Page 78
"After two or three minutes, carefully measure the temperature of the water at the top of the jar ... Also measure the temperature at the bottom."
(Answer: The water at the top will be just a little warmer)

Page 81
"Draw the energy chain showing the energy transfer from hot to cold water."
(Answer: Hot water ——> cold water)

Page 89
"How do you know energy is being transferred?"
(Answer: I can feel the heat.)

Page 90
"What do these results tell you about food and energy?"
(Answer: Food has potential energy.)

Page 97
"What variable are you investigating?"
(Answer: Light)

Page 98
"How is the grass grown in the dark different from the grass grown in the light?"
(Answer: It is turning yellow.)

"Which plants do you think are going to survive? ... Why do you think so?"
(Answer: Those grown in the light. Because they need light.)

Page 99
"What made the difference?"
(Answer: The light.)

"Did the fertilizer make any difference?"
(Answer: No, the grass grown in the dark still turned yellow and died.)

Page 102
"Which population is the largest?
(Answer: Seeds and grass).

Page 103
Which population is the smallest?"
(In this sample dialog cats would be the correct answer.)

"What would happen if they did not?"
(Answer: They would either move to a new location to find food or they would die.)

"How many crickets on the average would one frog eat per day?"
(Answer 90 ÷ 10 = 9 crickets.)

"If one cricket eat 15 seeds per day, how many seeds would be needed to support a frog for one day?"
(Answer: 9 x 15 = 135 seeds.)

"For a frog to survive one week how many seeds would need to be in the area?"
(Answer: 7 x 135 = 945 seeds per week.)

Page 106
"Why did you put water in three and no water in three?"
(Answer: To see if water is a relevant variable.)

Page 107
"What do you observe that you were not able to observe before?"
(Answer: A terrible smell.)

Page 109
"What variable are you investigating?"
(Answer: The materials left from decomposition.)

"What is it that these organisms do?"
(Answer: Decompose other organisms.)

Page 114
"What do the plants depend upon?"
(Answer: The raw materials and sunlight.)

"What is in the middle section of the chart? And what do they depend upon for food?"
(Answer: The plant eaters depend upon plants for food.)

"What about the top section?"
(Answer: They are animal eaters; they depend upon the plants.)

"What do the arrows show?"
(Answer: The transfer of food energy.)

"What role do the decomposers play in a community?"
(They break down dead plants and animals into raw materials.)